Macbeth

THE TRAGEDY OF
Macbeth

BY WILLIAM SHAKESPEARE

WITH INTERTEXTUAL COMMENTARY
BY WILLIAM W. MAIN

 THE ODYSSEY PRESS · INC. · New York

Contents

Introduction

THIS EDITION of *Macbeth* provides the reader with the standard Globe text and a built-in commentary. The content of the commentary is interpretive; its direct purpose is to illuminate meaning. Indirectly, an instructive purpose may be served as well, to refine the vision and to enlarge the eye, so that one can see better and see more when he reads *Macbeth*. The trained eye makes visible the relationships of contrast, comparison, and consequence. These relationships, in turn, reveal the very face of the play, its ironic complexion and tragic profile.

It is unwise to make a formula for interpreting literature; yet I will risk suggesting some techniques for critical reading. First, connect. Connect a part (a character, event, image, or theme) to another part by comparison or contrast; or connect a part to the whole by cause and effect. For example, the theme of time begins in an image of growth in Act I, "the seeds of time," and ends in an image of decay in Act V, "the sear, the yellow leaf." Again, the character Lady Macbeth warns Macbeth of going mad and ironically goes to pieces herself. The part itself may reflect the whole as does Lady Macbeth's sleepwalking in darkness epitomize her entire life. The structure of a play is made up of these various relationships.

Second, explicate. Explicate images, allusions, and symbols. Images of light and darkness, for example, often represent good and evil or clear reason and obscured reason; a burning candle symbolizes truth; an allusion to Hecate is demonic and an allusion to a chalice is divine. Shakespeare communicates directly through dramatic action, indirectly through poetic imagery. For example, Macbeth kills Duncan with a bloody dagger and then the ocean turns red. The imagery has magnified and intensified the dramatic action. In the analysis of imagery, the temptation is to make the images more important than the dramatic action. The best corrective for keeping a sense of proportion is to accept Aristotle's dictum that plot and character are more important than rhetoric and diction.

Third, evaluate. Evaluate the development of the action and the characters, especially their motives and means. Irony and tragedy are impossible without a value system that determines not only what a character is (a king or a queen), but what the character is worth (a traitor or a temptress). Macbeth's life is ironic because he assumes that fair is foul and foul is fair. In such a system of reversed moral values, the more Macbeth gains, the more he ironically loses.

Perhaps the underlying principle of these three suggestions for critical reading is that one should read a given passage as a fact, and then read it as a dramatic relationship. In this way one not only has an account of the facts but he can also account for the facts. The bane of many commentaries, often paraphrases of the facts padded with historical or biographical digressions, is thereby avoided. Like an experienced card player, a perceptive reader knows what his cards are and he knows what his cards are worth. He is not left helpless with facts, because the facts have now taken up the strength of value.

THE FORM OF THE COMMENTARY

The form of the commentary is intertexual; that is, it is inserted immediately after a given portion of the text. Commentaries are conventionally given in the introduction, in end notes, or mixed with eye-squinting footnotes. Such commentaries are frequently neglected, overlooked, or forgotten. To prevent these hazards and to take advantage of the immediate dramatic moment when the reader's mind and emotions are involved, I have placed the commentaries on the spot, where the action happens and the attention is fresh. The disadvantage of an interrupted text is outweighed, I feel, by the advantage of immediacy.

The ommission of explanatory footnotes will seeem critical to some, of less importance to others. Shakespeare, I feel, is too often overglossed; for example, "lily-liver'd" needlessly glossed as "white-livered and cowardly" because the liver was the seat of courage in the old physiology, or Macbeth's drink glossed as "warm spiced wine." Such gratuitous explanations add either something obvious or nothing vital to our understanding of the play. Communication in stage performances succeeds without such glosses. Yet some vocabulary glosses are valid, such as explaining "luxurious" as lustful or "fell" as cruel. Familiar words may carry an unfamiliar meaning. A minimum glossary, therefore, is included at the end of this edition.

An appendix of the dominant imagery is included for the reader who is interested in correlating the dramatic action with the poetic imagery. Act, scene, and line references are considered unnecessary except for cross-references to passages before or after the immediate passage under discussion.

THE PROBLEM OF INTERPRETATION

Since literature is not a maidenly matter of gathering facts but a disquieting and complicated matter of interpretation, the reader must make sense rather than find sense in a play. He must turn facts into patterns of thought and meaning. However, when he seeks to relate facts into patterns, proportion, and perspective, he is no longer objective but at once subjective and selective, revealing his own value system. Clinical detachment must give way to involvement, to a belief in what matters and to an involvement that demands one's intellectual and moral assent or dissent and his emotional sympathy or antipathy. The intelligent

Nietzsche went beyond intelligence when he said that the question of knowledge "becomes serious only if the question of values is answered."

The problem of interpretation is always problematical; it is never definitively solved, never closed. As Eric Heller has so wisely observed, "In literature as elsewhere there is no wisdom in *making* sure. There are only wise and unwise ways of being sure and not quite so sure, useful or useless ways of debating convictions and uncertainties." Certainly the unwise and useless ways of interpreting a comedy or a tragedy are those that are limited by dogmatic adhesions (Shakespeare is a Protestant or a Catholic), by doctrinal addictions (Shakespeare is a secular humanist), by polemical fancies (Shakespeare has no philosophy whatsoever), or by any other form of special pleading (such as Freudianism) that may ease the critic's heart and display his erudition. Even after one has patiently labored through a play without succumbing to aesthetic anagrams or historical genealogies and has arrived at a plausible interpretation of reality, he is haunted by the irony of whether he has found dark reality or merely reality darkly seen. Belief, unfortunately, can do more than change water into wine. For the resolutely confused, it can turn black into white.

Ironically, I am guilty of special pleading myself. My plea is to avoid special pleading, whether it be by a doublet-and-hose incognito or by the latest mescalin vision. Any source of knowledge, whether it be from the past or present, is welcome, provided its partial perspective does not obscure the total picture. The danger is that we, like God, create Shakespeare in our own insulated image. Were any of us the least like God, this saintly presumption would not be dangerous. The only safeguard I have against all forms of sophisticated provinciality is Ben Jonson's tribute to Shakespeare. "He was not of an age, but for all time!" All great artists transcend the world of change, but not all critics are full-stomached enough to face the timeless, transcendent content of art—the ironic and tragic vision that reveals human folly, meanness, and nobility. Readers of Shakespeare who have not discovered in the plays the reality of evil, the power of love, or the way to truth have largely wasted their time on precious trifles or on scholarly weight-lifting. My central plea, therefore, is to abolish the provincial view that makes art "of an age" only, and not also "for all time!" The criterion for great literature is that it be permanently contemporaneous, like the stars. Being the child of an age, I fully realize I cannot achieve the perspective of "all time." The best I can do is to be aware that whatever truth I do find is a foreshortened truth.

We are all indebted to the minds of the past; I shall be equally indebted to those that follow me and correct my opinions.

BIBLIOGRAPHICAL SUGGESTIONS

Written probably in 1606, *Macbeth* was first printed in the First Folio of 1623. The text is unfortunately marred by corruptions, still disputed, and by patent interpolations. The play was first performed at the Globe Theater and later at court. Shakespeare's chief source is Holinshed's *Chronicles of Scotland,* which gives a semi-legendary account of the reigns of Duncan and of Macbeth (1034-1057). Perhaps the most useful scholarly edition of the play is the Arden Edition of *Macbeth,* edited by Kenneth Muir, Cambridge, Harvard University Press, 1951/1957.

The following books and essays suggest only the boundaries of the abundant bibliography on *Macbeth.* An elaborate study of the historical background is found in Henry N. Paul, *The Royal Play of Macbeth,* New York, Macmillan, 1950. A detailed analysis of the workings of grace in the play is G. R. Elliott, *Dramatic Providence in Macbeth,* Princeton, Princeton University Press, 1958. Another noteworthy, fulllength study is Roy Walker, *The Time Is Free,* New York, Macmillan, 1949. A final book-length study, treating the play as a detective story, is David Baird, *The Thane of Cawdor,* London, Oxford University Press, 1937. A detailed study of the demonic metaphysics of the play is contained in Walter Clyde Curry, *Shakespeare's Philosophical Patterns,* Baton Rouge, Louisiana State University Press, 1937/1959.

Excellent essays on the play are numerous. One of the most famous, available in anthologies of Romantic literature, is Thomas De Quincey, "On the Knocking at the Gate in *Macbeth,*" 1823. A culmination of the romantic emphasis on character creation is found in Chapter IX of A. C. Bradley, *Shakespearean Tragedy,* London, Macmillan, 1904/1955. Representing imaginative interpretation of poetic symbolism are two books by G. Wilson Knight; Chapter V in *The Imperial Theme,* London, Methuen and Co., Ltd., 1931/1951, and Chapters VI and VII in *Wheel of Fire,* Methuen, 1949. A distinguished essay, "The Naked Babe and the Cloak of Manliness," which contrasts essential humanity and stripped humanity, is Chapter II of Cleanth Brooks, *The Well Wrought Urn,* New York, Reynal and Hitchcock, 1947. The diversity of the bibliography on *Macbeth* affirms the richness of the play.

Macbeth

Macbeth

DRAMATIS PERSONAE

DUNCAN, *king of Scotland*

MALCOLM,
DONALBAIN, } *his sons*

MACBETH,
BANQUO, } *generals of the king's army*

MACDUFF,
LENNOX,
ROSS,
MENTEITH } *noblemen of Scotland*
ANGUS,
CAITHNESS,

FLEANCE, *son to* BANQUO

SIWARD, *Earl of Northumberland, general of the English forces*

Young SIWARD, *his son*

SEYTON, *an officer attending on* MACBETH

Boy, son to MACDUFF

An English Doctor

A Scotch Doctor

A Soldier

A Porter
An Old Man

LADY MACBETH
LADY MACDUFF
Gentlewoman attending on LADY MACBETH

HECATE
Three Witches
Apparitions

Lords, Gentlemen, Officers, Soldiers, Murderers, Attendants,
and Messengers

SCENE: *Scotland: England*

ACT I

Scene I: A desert place.

Thunder and lightning. Enter three Witches.

FIRST WITCH. When shall we three meet again
   In thunder, lightning, or in rain?
SECOND WITCH. When the hurlyburly's done,
   When the battle's lost and won.
THIRD WITCH. That will be ere the set of sun.   5
FIRST WITCH. Where the place?
SECOND WITCH.   Upon the heath.
THIRD WITCH. There to meet with Macbeth.
FIRST WITCH. I come, Graymalkin!
SECOND WITCH. Paddock calls.
SECOND WITCH. Anon.   10
ALL. Fair is foul, and foul is fair:
   Hover through the fog and filthy air. (*Exeunt*)

The Witches Meet   I.i.

*The witches, who are soon to be Macbeth's tempters, will be
fatally misunderstood by their chief victim, Macbeth. They will
know Macbeth's deep desires better than Macbeth will know
theirs. When the witches do encounter Macbeth shortly, these
satanic liars will deceive him with half-truths and equivocations,
tempting him to seize sovereign power. In this opening scene
the witches are prophesying a battle won, which ironically for
Macbeth will become a battle lost. Hence they make foul appear
fair. Foul themselves, they will transform the fair Macbeth into
a foul hypocrite and monster. Allied with animals (Graymalkin is
a cat and Paddock a toad), the witches are subhuman creatures
that bestialize man's nature.*

*Nature herself is not smiling on these arch-liars; ominous thun-
der and lightning reveal a sterile heath. The scene is judgmental
and prophetic of doom. Clouded reason and obscured truth are
expressed in the naturalistic symbols of "fog and filthy air."
Wherever the witches are headed, foul weather is easily pre-
dicted.*

Scene II: *A camp near Forres.*

Alarum within. Enter DUNCAN, MALCOM, DONALBAIN, LENNOX,
with Attendants, *meeting a bleeding* Sergeant.

DUNCAN. What bloody man is that? He can report,
As seemeth by his plight, of the revolt
The newest state.
MALCOLM.   This is the sergeant
Who like a good and hardy soldier fought
'Gainst my captivity. Hail, brave friend!   5
Say to the king the knowledge of the broil
As thou didst leave it.
SERGEANT.   Doubtful it stood:
As two spent swimmers, that do cling together
And choke their art. The merciless Macdonwald—
Worthy to be a rebel, for to that   10
The multiplying villanies of nature

Do swarm upon him—from the western isles
Of kerns and gallowglasses is supplied;
And fortune, on his damned quarrel smiling,
Show'd like a rebel's whore: but all's too weak: 15
For brave Macbeth—well he deserves that name—
Disdaining fortune, with his brandish'd steel,
Which smoked with bloody execution,
Like valour's minion carved out his passage
Till he faced the slave;   20
Which ne'er shook hands, nor bade farewell to him,
Till he unseam'd him from the nave to the chaps,
And fix'd his head upon our battlements.

DUNCAN. O valiant cousin! worthy gentleman!

SERGEANT. As whence the sun 'gins his reflection   25
Shipwrecking storms and direful thunders break,
So from that spring whence comfort seem'd to come
Discomfort swells. Mark, king of Scotland, mark:
No sooner justice had with valour arm'd
Compell'd these skipping kerns to trust their heels,   30
But the Norweyan lord surveying vantage,
With furbish'd arms and new supplies of men
Began a fresh assault.

DUNCAN.   Dismay'd not this
Our captains, Macbeth and Banquo?

SERGEANT.   '   Yes;
As sparrows eagles, or the hare the lion.   35
If I say sooth, I must report they were
As cannons overcharged with double cracks, so they
Doubly redoubled strokes upon the foe:
Except they meant to bathe in reeking wounds,
Or memorize another Golgotha,   40
I cannot tell.
But I am faint, my gashes cry for help.

DUNCAN. So well thy words become thee as thy wounds;
They smack of honour both. Go get him surgeons.

                              (*Exit Sergeant, attended*)

Who comes here?

(*Enter* ROSS)

MALCOLM. The worthy thane of Ross.   45

LENNOX. What a haste looks through his eyes! So should he look
That seems to speak things strange.

ROSS.   God Save the king!

DUNCAN. Whence camest thou, worthy thane?

ROSS.   From Fife, great
 king;
Where the Norweyan banners flout the sky
And fan our people cold. Norway himself,   50
With terrible numbers,
Assisted by that most disloyal traitor
The thane of Cawdor, began a dismal conflict;
Till that Bellona's bridegroom, lapp'd in proof,
Confronted him with self-comparisons,   55
Point against point rebellious, arm 'gainst arm,
Curbing his lavish spirit: and, to conclude,
The victory fell on us.

DUNCAN.   Great happiness!

ROSS.   That now
Sweno, the Norways' king, craves composition;
Nor would we deign him burial of his men   60
Till he disbursed at Saint Colme's inch
Ten thousand dollars to our general use.

DUNCAN. No more that thane of Cawdor shall deceive
Our bosom interest: go pronounce his present death,
And with his former title greet Macbeth.   65

ROSS. I'll see it done.

DUNCAN. What he hath lost noble Macbeth hath won. (*Exeunt*)

The Noble Macbeth   *I.ii.*

*The initial picture of the soldier Macbeth is free from any cor-
ruption. He is praised as "brave Macbeth," "valiant cousin," and
"noble Macbeth." Here is a hero with an obedient will and an
untainted knowledge who fights loyally for his king, slaying the*

rebel Macdonwald and vanquishing "that most disloyal traitor/
The thane of Cawdor." Traitors and rebels are destroyed by "jus-
tice . . . with valor arm'd."

Yet this initial picture of noble heroism will be turned inside
out, into ignoble villainy. Macbeth valiantly kills a traitor who
has deceived King Duncan and Duncan awards Macbeth the
traitor's title, thane of Cawdor. "What he hath lost noble Macbeth hath won." Indeed he has. Macbeth will win everything his
disloyal predecessor lost: his title, his loyalty, and literally his
head. Macbeth kills a traitor and will become a traitor. Losing
and winning become ambiguous. Yet justice is unambiguous. As
Macbeth, in the name of justice here fixes the rebel Macdonwald's head on the battlements, so will Macduff later do the same
to Macbeth in the name of justice.

In the beginning, however, there is no ambiguity. Foul is foul
as seen in the witches, and fair is fair as seen in Macbeth. He is
compared to the king of birds, the eagle, and to the king of
beasts, the lion. As the bridegroom of Bellona (the Roman goddess of war), Macbeth is unafraid of blood and fortune. Ironically, it is Macbeth's very fearless valor and success in war that
makes him vulnerable to temptations of power. In short, had
Macbeth not successfully won the title of thane of Cawdor, the
witches would never have planned their rendezvous with him.

Scene III: A heath near Forres.

Thunder. Enter the three Witches.

FIRST WITCH. Where hast thou been, sister?
SECOND WITCH. Killing swine.
THIRD WITCH. Sister, where thou?
FIRST WITCH. A sailor's wife had chestnuts in her lap,
    And munch'd, and munch'd, and munch'd:—"Give me,"
        quoth I: 5
    "Aroint thee, witch!" the rump-fed ronyon cries.
    Her husband's to Aleppo gone, master o' the Tiger:
    But in a sieve I'll thither sail,
    And, like a rat without a tail,

I'll do, I'll do, and I'll do.   10
SECOND WITCH. I'll give thee a wind.
FIRST WITCH. Thou 'rt kind.
THIRD WITCH. And I another.
FIRST WITCH. I myself have all the other,
   And the very ports they blow,   15
   All the quarters that they know
   I' the shipman's card.
   I will drain him dry as hay:
   Sleep shall neither night nor day
   Hang upon his pent-house lid;   20
   He shall live a man forbid:
   Weary se'nnights nine times nine
   Shall he dwindle, peak and pine:
   Though his bark cannot be lost,
   Yet it shall be tempest-tost.   25
   Look what I have.
SECOND WITCH. Show me, show me.
FIRST WITCH. Here I have a pilot's thumb,
   Wreck'd as homeward he did come. (*Drum within*)
THIRD WITCH. A drum, a drum!   30
   Macbeth doth come.
ALL. The weird sisters, hand in hand,
   Posters of the sea and land,
   Thus do go about, about:
   Thrice to thine and thrice to mine   35
   And thrice again, to make up nine.
   Peace! the charm's wound up.

The Charm Prepared   *I.iii.1-37*

*Like the "tempest-tost" sailor accursed and wrecked by the
vindictive First Witch, Macbeth too "shall live a man forbid"
(i.e., accursed) without rest or sleep. The witches have wound
up their magic charm, so that foul will seem fair. Only when the
charm becomes unwound will Macbeth discover his charmed life
is not really charmed.*

An ominous booming drum introduces Macbeth to the tempta-

tions of the witches, who are again associated with animals (swine and rats), as well as with magic (the charm that ticks like a high-explosive time-bomb). The black magic of deception will transform Macbeth into a beast and Scotland into a terrified jungle.

(*Enter* MACBETH *and* BANQUO)

MACBETH. So foul and fair a day I have not seen.

BANQUO. How far is 't call'd to Forres? What are these
  So wither'd and so wild in their attire,   40
  That look not like the inhabitants o' the earth,
  And yet are on 't? Live you? or are you aught
  That man may question? You seem to understand me,
  By each at once her choppy finger laying
  Upon her skinny lips: you should be women,   45
  And yet your beards forbid me to interpret
  That you are so.

MACBETH.   Speak, if you can: what are you?

FIRST WITCH. All hail, Macbeth! hail to thee, thane of Glamis!

SECOND WITCH. All hail, Macbeth! hail to thee, thane of Cawdor!

THIRD WITCH. All hail, Macbeth, that shalt be king hereafter!   50

BANQUO. Good sir, why do you start; and seem to fear
  Things that do sound so fair? I' the name of truth,
  Are ye fantastical, or that indeed
  Which outwardly ye show? My noble partner
  You greet with present grace and great prediction   55
  Of noble having and of royal hope,
  That he seems rapt withal: to me you speak not.
  If you can look into the seeds of time,
  And say which grain will grow and which will not,
  Speak then to me, who neither beg nor fear   60
  Your favours nor your hate.

FIRST WITCH. Hail!

SECOND WITCH. Hail!

THIRD WITCH. Hail!

FIRST WITCH. Lesser than Macbeth, and greater.   65

SECOND WITCH. Not so happy, yet much happier.

THIRD WITCH. Thou shalt get kings, though thou be none:
So all hail, Macbeth and Banquo!
FIRST WITCH. Banquo and Macbeth, all hail!
MACBETH. Stay, you imperfect speakers, tell me more: 70
By Sinel's death I know I am thane of Glamis;
But how of Cawdor? the thane of Cawdor lives,
A prosperous gentleman; and to be king
Stands not within the prospect of belief,
No more than to be Cawdor. Say from whence 75
You owe this strange intelligence? or why
Upon this blasted heath you stop our way
With such prophetic greeting? Speak, I charge you. (*Witches vanish*)
BANQUO. The earth hath bubbles, as the water has,
And these are of them. Whither are they vanish'd? 80
MACBETH. Into the air; and what seem'd corporal melted
As breath into the wind. Would they had stay'd!
BANQUO. Were such things here as we do speak about?
Or have we eaten on the insane root
That takes the reason prisoner? 85
MACBETH. Your children shall be kings.
BANQUO. You shall be king.
MACBETH. And thane of Cawdor too: went it not so?
BANQUO. To the selfsame tune and words. Who's here?

The Witches' Prophecy   *I.iii.38-88*

The witches, those connoisseurs of deception, especially self-deception, tell the truth but not the whole truth. Truth is seeing all things in their proper proportion, and Macbeth sees only foreshortened truth. With their "strange intelligence" these "imperfect speakers" mislead Macbeth into thinking foul is fair. They say he will be king, but they do not say he will murder a king to become king. They reveal fair ends but conceal foul means. Curious and troubled, Macbeth swallows the witches' poisonous suggestion, which is psychologically an auto-suggestion. Regardless, suggestibility can change this man into a monster.

Banquo is right when he says he and Macbeth may have "eaten on the insane root/That takes the reason prisoner."

The physical appearance of the witches is itself equivocal: women with beards. They speak in riddles. "Not so happy, yet much happier." Despite Macbeth's battle victories on this day, he smells the foul weather the witches had spoken of in the beginning. "So foul and fair a day I have not seen," says Macbeth.

The major theme and image of time is stressed by Banquo, who asks the witches which grains of "the seeds of time" will grow. Time is not mere transitoriness. It contains hope and despair and will bring winners and losers "When the hurlyburly's done" (I.i.3). Time brings permanent consequences. And the first growth from "the seeds of time" is as much "the insane root/That takes the reason prisoner" as the new title of thane of Cawdor.

(*Enter* ROSS *and* ANGUS)

ROSS. The king hath happily received, Macbeth,
 The news of thy success; and when he reads   90
 Thy personal venture in the rebels' fight,
 His wonders and his praises do contend
 Which should be thine or his: silenced with that,
 In viewing o'er the rest o' the selfsame day,
 He finds thee in the stout Norweyan ranks,   95
 Nothing afeard of what thyself didst make,
 Strange images of death. As thick as hail
 Came post with post; and every one did bear
 Thy praises in his kingdom's great defence,
 And pour'd them down before him.
ANGUS.   We are sent   100
 To give thee from our royal master thanks;
 Only to herald thee into his sight,
 Not pay thee.
ROSS. And, for an earnest of a greater honour,
 He bade me, from him, call thee thane of Cawdor: 105
 In which addition, hail, most worthy thane!
 For it is thine.
BANQUO.   What, can the devil speak true?

MACBETH. The thane of Cawdor lives: why do you dress me
  In borrow'd robes?

ANGUS.   Who was the thane lives yet;
  But under heavy judgement bears that life   110
  Which he deserves to lose. Whether he was combined
  With those of Norway, or did line the rebel
  With hidden help and vantage, or that with both
  He labour'd in his country's wreck, I know not;
  But treasons capital, confess'd and proved,   115
  Have overthrown him.

MACBETH.   *(aside)*. Glamis, and thane of Cawdor!
  The greatest is behind. (*To* ROSS *and* ANGUS) Thanks for
    your pains.
  (*To* BANQUO) Do you not hope your children shall be kings,
  When those that gave the thane of Cawdor to me
  Promised no less to them?

BANQUO.   That trusted home   120
  Might yet enkindle you unto the crown,
  Besides the thane of Cawdor. But 'tis strange:
  And oftentimes, to win us to our harm,
  The instruments of darkness tell us truths,
  Win us with honest trifles, to betray's   125
  In deepest consequence.
  Cousins, a word, I pray you.

MACBETH.   *(aside)*. Two truths are told,
  As happy prologues to the swelling act
  Of the imperial theme.—I thank you, gentlemen.
  (*Aside*) This supernatural soliciting
  Cannot be ill, cannot be good: if ill,
  Why hath it given me earnest of success,
  Commencing in a truth? I am thane of Cawdor:
  If good, why do I yield to that suggestion
  Whose horrid image doth unfix my hair   135
  And make my seated heart knock at my ribs,
  Against the use of nature? Present fears
  Are less than horrible imaginings:
  My thought, whose murder yet is but fantastical,
  Shakes so my single state of man that function   140

Is smother'd in surmise, and nothing is
But what is not.

BANQUO.   Look, how our partner's rapt.

MACBETH (*aside*). If chance will have me king, why, chance may
    crown me,
Without my stir.

BANQUO.   New honours come up him,
Like our strange garments, cleave not to their mould   145
But with the aid of use.

MACBETH   (*aside*). Come what come may,
Time and the hour runs through the roughest day.

BANQUO. Worthy Macbeth, we stay upon your leisure.

MACBETH. Give me your favour: my dull brain was wrought
With things forgotten. Kind gentlemen, your pains   150
Are register'd where every day I turn
The leaf to read them. Let us toward the king.
Think upon what hath chanced, and, at more time,
The interim having weigh'd it, let us speak
Our free hearts each to other.

BANQUO.   Very gladly.   155

MACBETH. Till then, enough. Come, friends. *(Exeunt)*

Macbeth's Warning   *I.iii.89-156*

The temptation to become king, "the imperial theme," is think-
able and unthinkable. Two out of three of the witches' prophecies
have lawfully come true; Macbeth has won the titles of Glamis
and Cawdor. The flush of success is heady stuff; becoming "king
hereafter" seems a sane possibility, but only to a man who has
"eaten on the insane root" (I.iii.84). It is madness for Macbeth
to try to out-reason "the devil" or to rationalize the witches'
"supernatural soliciting." The witches' prophecy is in reality a
prophecy of murder, and Macbeth instinctively knows it through
his "horrible imaginings." His hair stands on end and his heart
knocks at his ribs "Against the use of nature." Banquo warns
Macbeth against "The instruments of darkness" that betray a
man "In deepest consequence." Macbeth is further warned by
the example of the rebel thane of Cawdor whose "treasons

capital" *destroyed him. Macbeth even thinks of leaving the future all to chance. Despite all warnings and terrors, Macbeth continues to think the unthinkable. Reasoning with temptation always gives the devil an immense advantage.*

The clothes imagery of "borrowe'd robes" and strange garments" will become recurrent, suggesting the theft of power that Macbeth seizes and the false front of hypocrisy that Macbeth wears. Macbeth is a man who doesn't wear his own clothes. The theme of time is emphasized in Banquo's warning that the witches can "betray 's/In deepest consequence" and in Macbeth's fatalistic statement, "Come what may,/Time and the hour run through the roughest day." Time is more than time if it contains "deepest consequence" or eternity; that is, what happens in one moment of time happens permanently, forever. Macbeth is profoundly a play of "deepest consequence," of eternity growing out of "the seeds of time" (I.iii.58).

Scene IV: Forres. The palace.

Flourish. Enter DUNCAN, MALCOLM, DONALBAIN, LENNOX, *and* Attendants.

DUNCAN. Is execution done on Cawdor? Are not
　　Those in commission yet return'd?
MALCOLM.　　　　　　　　　　　My liege,
　　They are not yet come back. But I have spoke
　　With one that saw him die: who did report
　　That very frankly he confess'd his treasons,　　　　　5
　　Implor'd your highness' pardon and set forth
　　A deep repentance: nothing in his life
　　Became him like the leaving it; he died
　　As one that had been studied in his death
　　To throw away the dearest thing he owed,　　　　　10
　　As 'twere a careless trifle.
DUNCAN.　　　　　　　　There 's no art
　　To find the mind's construction in the face:
　　He was a gentleman on whom I built
　　An absolute trust.
(*Enter* MACBETH, BANQUO, ROSS, *and* ANGUS)

The First Thane of Cawdor Executed   I.iv.1-14

    The report of the death of the first thane of Cawdor, Macbeth's traitorous predecessor, provides a sharp contrast with the eventual death of the traitor Macbeth. The first Cawdor dies confessing "his treasons" and setting forth a "deep repentance." With such a reversal of will he dissolves his self-will, or autonomy, and becomes eligible for purgatory, the symbolic land of repentance and corrective reform. Macbeth, however, the inheritor of Cawdor's title, will persist in his rebel-willed autonomy and be permanently cut off from righteousness, lost in a land symbolically known as hell. Each traitor demonstrates, respectively, resolved irony (purgatory) and unresolved irony (hell), the irony being the failure of self-willed success. To epitomize Macbeth's life, he too threw away "the dearest thing [his soul or integrity] he owed [owned],/As 'twere a careless trifle."

    Macbeth's stage entrance here is itself a biting irony. Duncan says that the traitor Cawdor "was a gentleman on whom I built/An absolute trust." Although Duncan does not know it, here comes another trusted traitor: "Enter Macbeth."

                O worthiest cousin!
The sin of my ingratitude even now   15
Was heavy on me: thou art so far before
That swiftest wing of recompense is slow
To overtake thee. Would thou hadst less deserved,
That the proportion both of thanks and payment
Might have been mine! only I have left to say,   20
More is thy due than more than all can pay.
MACBETH. The service and the loyalty I owe,
In doing it, pays itself. Your highness' part
Is to receive our duties; and our duties
Are to your throne and state children and servants,   25
Which do but what they should, by doing every thing
Safe toward your love and honour.
DUNCAN.   Welcome hither:
I have begun to plant thee, and will labour

To make thee full of growing. Noble Banquo,
That hast no less deserved, nor must be known   30
No less to have done so, let me infold thee
And hold thee to my heart.

BANQUO.   There if I grow,
The harvest is your own.

DUNCAN.   My plenteous joys,
Wanton in fulness, seek to hide themselves
In drops of sorrow. Sons, kinsmen, thanes,   35
And you whose places are the nearest, know
We will establish our estate upon
Our eldest, Malcolm, whom we name hereafter
The Prince of Cumberland; which honour must
Not unaccompanied invest him only,   40
But signs of nobleness, like stars, shall shine
On all deservers. From hence to Inverness,
And bind us further to you.

MACBETH. The rest is labour, which is not used for you:
I'll be myself the harbinger and make joyful   45
The hearing of my wife with your approach;
So humbly take my leave.

DUNCAN.   My worthy Cawdor!

MACBETH (*aside*). The Prince of Cumberland! that is a step
On which I must fall down, or else o'erleap,
For in my way it lies. Stars, hide your fires;   50
Let not light see my black and deep desires:
The eye wink at the hand; yet let that be,
Which the eye fears, when it is done, to see. (*Exit*)

DUNCAN. True, worthy Banquo; he is full so valiant,
And in his commendations I am fed;   55
It is a banquet to me. Let's after him,
Whose care is gone before to bid us welcome:
It is a peerless kinsman. (*Flourish. Exeunt*)

Hidden Fires   *I.iv.14-58*

     The witches had said that Macbeth "shalt be king hereafter!"
(I.iii.50). Duncan here announces his successor, "Our eldest, Mal-

*colm, whom we name hereafter/The Prince of Cumberland." If
Duncan is right, the witches must have been wrong, for they
named Macbeth, not Malcolm. Only by defying Duncan can
Macbeth make the witches' evil prophecy come true. Macbeth
must "o'erleap" the "step" of Malcolm. By depersonalizing a person into a step, Macbeth is sure of becoming a step himself. Although Malcolm's royal appointment is an unexpected obstacle,
Duncan's journey to Macbeth's castle is an unexpected opportunity—for murder. Such is the kind of "chance" that may crown
Macbeth (I.iii.143).*

*The imagery of the stars indicates the magnitude and nature
of Macbeth's planned murder of Duncan. So colossal is the deed
that even the stars in heaven are involved. It was the old belief
that the fixed stars were ruled by the cherubim, the angels of
knowledge. Hence Macbeth asks the knowing stars to hide their
fires, symbolically the light of truth. In hiding the stars, the true
guides of action here, Macbeth is in effect deliberately obscuring
his own better wisdom. The deed of murder must be done in the
dark, that is, in an evil undercover "which the eye fears, when
it is done, to see." Darkness here is not so much a symbol of the
ignorance of knowledge but of the perversion of the truth. So
long as Macbeth remains Duncan's "peerless kinsman," Macbeth's
"nobleness, like stars, shall shine," and Duncan shall make Macbeth "full of growing." However, the benign fate of the stars becomes a malignant fate when Macbeth becomes Duncan's peerless traitor. If the angels shudder to hear Macbeth's evil thoughts,
the witches gloat.*

Scene V: Inverness MACBETH'S *castle.*

Enter LADY MACBETH, *reading a letter.*

LADY MACBETH. "They met me in the day of success; and I have
learned by the perfectest report, they have more in them than
mortal knowledge. When I burned in desire to question them
further, they made themselves air, into which they vanished.
Whiles I stood rapt in wonder of it, came missives from the

king, who all-hailed me 'Thane of Cawdor'; by which title, before, these weird sisters saluted me, and referred me to the coming on of time, with 'Hail, king that shalt be!' This have I thought good to deliver thee, my dearest partner of greatness, that thou mightst not lose the dues of rejoicing, by being ignorant of what greatness is promised thee. Lay it to thy heart, and farewell."

Glamis thou art, and Cawdor; and shalt be
What thou art promised: yet do I fear thy nature;
It is too full o' the milk of human kindness
To catch the nearest way: thou wouldst be great;
Art not without ambition, but without   20
The illness should attend it: what thou wouldst highly,
That wouldst thou holily; wouldst not play false,
And yet wouldst wrongly win: thou 'ldst have, great Glamis,
That which cries "Thus thou must do, if thou have it;
And that which rather thou dost fear to do   25
Than wishest should be undone." Hie thee hither,
That I may pour my spirits in thine ear;
And chastise with the valour of my tongue
All that impedes thee from the golden round,
Which fate and metaphysical aid doth seem   30
To have thee crown'd withal.

Macbeth's Letter   *I.v.1-31*

*Lady Macbeth's reaction is an impure mixture of joy and fear.
She rejoices over the witches' prophecy, but fears Macbeth's nature, "too full o' the milk of human kindness" to "play false" and
grasp "the golden round." Clearly, she must corrupt her husband's honest nature and curdle the milk, for Macbeth is not evil
by nature. By pouring her poisonous spirits into Macbeth's ear,
she will tempt him to murder rather than restrain him. In short,
there are more than three witches tempting Macbeth; the fourth
is Lady Macbeth herself. If the three witches tempt Macbeth
with equivocal knowledge, Lady Macbeth is ready to tempt him
with a malicious will.*

(*Enter a* Messenger)
                          What is your tidings?

MESSENGER. The king comes here to-night.

LADY MACBETH.   Thou 'rt mad to say it:
  Is not thy master with him? who, were 't so,
  Would have inform'd for preparation.

MESSENGER. So please you, it is true: our thane is coming: 35
  One of my fellows had the speed of him,
  Who, almost dead for breath, had scarcely more
  Than would make up his message.

LADY MACBETH.   Give him tending;
  He brings great news. (*Exit Messenger*)
                          The raven himself is hoarse
  That croaks the fatal entrance of Duncan   40
  Under my battlements. Come, you spirits
  That tend on mortal thoughts, unsex me here,
  And fill me from the crown to the toe top-full
  Of direst cruelty! make thick my blood;
  Stop up the access and passage to remorse,   45
  That no compunctious visitings of nature
  Shake my fell purpose, nor keep peace between
  The effect and it! Come to my woman's breasts,
  And take my milk for gall, you murdering ministers,
  Wherever in your sightless substances   50
  You wait on nature's mischief! Come, thick night,
  And pall thee in the dunnest smoke of hell,
  That my keen knife see not the wound it makes,
  Nor heaven peep through the blanket of the dark,
  To cry "Hold, hold!"

(*Enter* MACBETH)
                          Great Glamis! worthy Cawdor!   55
  Greater than both, by the all-hail hereafter!
  Thy letters have transported me beyond
  This ignorant present, and I feel now
  The future in the instant.

MACBETH.   My dearest love,

Duncan comes here to-night.

LADY MACBETH.   And when goes hence?   60

MACBETH. To-morrow, as he purposes.

LADY MACBETH.   O, never
Shall sun that morrow see!
Your face, my thane, is as a book where men
May read strange matters. To beguile the time,
Look like the time; bear welcome in your eye,   65
Your hand, your tongue: look like the innocent flower,
But be the serpent under 't. He that's coming
Must be provided for: and you shall put
This night's great business into my dispatch;
Which shall to all our nights and days to come   70
Give solely sovereign sway and masterdom.

MACBETH. We will speak further.

LADY MACBETH.   Only look up clear;
To alter favour ever is to fear:
Leave all the rest to me. (*Exeunt*)

Lady Macbeth's Denaturalization   *I.v.31-74*

Lady Macbeth takes command; Macbeth listens. According to degree of authority Macbeth as a subject should obey the king, and Lady Macbeth as a wife should obey the husband. Instead, this hierarchy of rank is fatally twisted. Macbeth will disobey his king, and obey his wife. This reversal of allegiance helps explain the ensuing disaster.

To steel herself for the murder of Duncan, Lady Macbeth must, in effect, turn herself into a witch. She must denaturalize herself for fear that "compunctious visitings of nature/Shake [her] fell purpose." This abuse of her nature is expressed in imagery of nature. The sensitivity of nature must be desensitized. Just as a dentist would numb a tooth before drilling, so does Lady Macbeth call upon "murdering ministers" to unsex her, to fill her with "direst cruelty," to thicken her blood, to change her milk to gall, and to thicken night "in the dunnest smoke of hell." Now her "keen knife" will not see "the wound it makes." As Macbeth hid the stars, Lady Macbeth hides heaven in a "blanket of dark." The murders must go against their own nature and the natural order, to commit murder. The effect of the crime on nature is ironically prophesied by Lady Macbeth. "O, never/Shall sun that morrow see!" The morning after the crime the sun does not come up (II.iv.).

Scene VI: Before MACBETH's *castle.*

Hautboys and torches. Enter DUNCAN, MALCOLM, DONALBAIN, BANQUO, LENNOX, MACDUFF, ROSS, ANGUS, *and* Attendants.

DUNCAN. This castle hath a pleasant seat; the air
    Nimbly and sweetly recommends itself
    Unto our gentle senses.
BANQUO.   This guest of summer,
    The temple-haunting martlet, does approve,
    By his loved mansionry, that the heaven's breath   5
    Smells wooingly here: no jutty, frieze,
    Buttress, nor coign of vantage, but this bird
    Hath made his pendent bed and procreant cradle:
    Where they most breed and haunt, I have observed,
    The air is delicate.

(*Enter* LADY MACBETH)
DUNCAN.   See, see, our honour'd hostess!   10
    The love that follows us sometime is our trouble,
    Which still we thank as love. Herein I teach you
    How you shall bid God 'ild us for your pains,
    And thank us for your trouble.
LADY MACBETH.   All our service
    In every point twice done and then done double   15
    Were poor and single business to contend
    Against those honours deep and broad wherewith
    Your majesty loads our house: for those of old,
    And the late dignities heap'd up to them,
    We rest your hermits.

DUNCAN. Where's the thane of Cawdor? 20
We coursed him at the heels, and had a purpose
To be his purveyor: but he rides well;
And his great love, sharp as his spur, hath holp him
To his home before us. Fair and noble hostess,
We are your guest to-night.

LADY MACBETH. Your servants ever 25
Have theirs, themselves and what is theirs, in compt,
To make their audit at your highness' pleasure,
Still to return your own.

DUNCAN. Give me your hand;
Conduct me to mine host: we love him highly,
And shall continue our graces towards him. 30
By your leave, hostess. (*Exeunt*)

Lady Macbeth Welcomes Duncan   *I.vi*

In the preceding scene Lady Macbeth told Macbeth to "look like the innocent flower,/But be the serpent under 't" (I,iv.66-67). In the present scene Lady Macbeth follows her own advice in welcoming Duncan. Throughout, foul appears fair. The castle appears pleasant, not sinister. The air appears sweet and delicate, not foggy and filthy (I.i.12). "The temple-haunting martlet" nests on the castle, not the croaking raven heard earlier (I.v.40). Here "heaven's breath/Smells wooingly," not like "the dunnest smoke of hell" (I.v.52). And finally Lady Macbeth appears as the "Fair and noble hostess," not the unsexed witch full of "direst cruelty" (I.v.44). Lady Macbeth beguiles before she bludgeons her victim. Duncan's presence consecrates the castle; Lady Macbeth's execrates it.

Scene VII: MACBETH's *castle.*

Hautboys and torches. Enter a Sewer, *and divers* Servants *with dishes and service, and pass over the stage. Then enter* MACBETH

MACBETH. If it were done when 'tis done, then 'twere well

It were done quickly: if the assassination
Could trammel up the consequence, and catch
With his surcease success; that but this blow
Might be the be-all and the end-all here,
But here, upon this bank and shoal of time,
We 'ld jump the life to come. But in these cases
We still have judgement here; that we but teach
Bloody instructions, which, being taught, return
To plague the inventor: this even-handed justice   10
Commends the ingredients of our poison'd chalice
To our own lips.

Macbeth's Gamble on Time   *I.vii.1-12*

Macbeth tries to outwit his conscience and to cheat time and its irrefutable consequences. He gambles that 'this bank and shoal of time" is the end, that there is no "life to come" after death. Ironically there is very little left to live for after the murder. Homicide brings a barren life. Consequence cannot be trammeled up. Time inevitably "Creeps in this petty pace from day to day" (V.v.20), bringing "deepest consequence" (I.iii.126). Time cannot be cheated. Time contains the permanence of eternity.

As a wishful amoralist Macbeth hopes that the assassination is self-terminating without returning "To plague the inventor." The conditional "if" betrays his wishful thinking. Yet Macbeth knows right from wrong, even if he wishes right and wrong did not exist. "We still have judgement here," and "this even-handed justice" returns the "poison'd chalice/To our own lips." The use of "chalice," the goblet used in the sacrament of the Lord's Supper, as the instrument of retributive justice points to justice coming from a divine or transhuman source. It is the transcendent perspective of "even-handed justice" outside "this bank and shoal of time" that makes Macbeth's gamble on self-willed autonomy ironic. Though Macbeth would live in a world of irresponsible might, there is no exit from the world of responsible right. Macbeth knows that conscience and judgment forbid the deed, that "even-handed justice" will punish the deed, and that treachery damns the deed (I.vii.12-20). There is no exit.

He's here in double trust;
First, as I am his kinsman and his subject,
Strong both against the deed; then, as his host,
Who should against his murderer shut the door,   15
Not bear the knife myself. Besides, this Duncan
Hath borne his faculties so meek, hath been
So clear in his great office, that his virtues
Will plead like angels, trumpet-tongued, against
The deep damnation of his taking-off;   20
And pity, like a naked new-born babe,
Striding the blast, or heaven's cherubim, horsed
Upon the sightless couriers of the air,
Shall blow the horrid deed in every eye,
That tears shall drown the wind. I have no spur   25
To prick the sides of my intent, but only
Vaulting ambition, which o'erleaps itself
And falls on the other.

Macbeth's Multiple Treacheries   *I.vii.12-28*

In Dante's Inferno, *the ninth circle of hell contains the fraud-
ulent who have broken a special trust. In this icy pit are found
the murderers of kindred and guests, and the traitors to country
and benefactors. As Duncan's kinsman, subject, host, and bene-
ficiary, Macbeth may achieve "deep damnation" in a single
treacherous stroke. Despite his conscience-struggle and dread of
"the horrid deed," Macbeth is sliding into an icy world of frozen
pity where treachery is the only law.*

*So heinous is the crime, Macbeth feels, that heaven itself will
reveal it to the world, particularly through the angels of knowledge, the cherubim. Macbeth seems ready to drop out of the race
between his own mount, "Vaulting ambition," and "heaven's
cherubim, horsed/Upon the sightless couriers of the air."*

*Earlier, the witches' temptation was announced with drums
(I.iii.30); now, the "trumpet-tongued" angels announce the consequences of "deep damnation." Macbeth has heard both drums
and trumpets. The blasting trumpets are disheartening.*

(*Enter* LADY MACBETH)

How now! what news?

LADY MACBETH. He has almost supp'd: why have you left the
chamber?

MACBETH. Hath he ask'd for me?

LADY MACBETH.   Know you not he has?   30

MACBETH. We will proceed no further in this business:
He hath honour'd me of late; and I have bought
Golden opinions from all sorts of people,
Which would be worn now in their newest gloss,
Not cast aside so soon.

LADY MACBETH.   Was the hope drunk   35
Wherein you dress'd yourself? hath it slept since?
And wakes it now, to look so green and pale
At what it did so freely? From this time
Such I account thy love. Art thou afeard
To be the same in thine own act and valour   40
As thou art in desire? Wouldst thou have that
Which thou esteem'st the ornament of life,
And live a coward in thine own esteem,
Letting "I dare not" wait upon "I would,"
Like the poor cat i' the adage?

MACBETH.   Prithee, peace: 45
I dare do all that may become a man;
Who dares do more is none.

LADY MACBETH.   What beast was't, then,
That made you break this enterprise to me?
When you durst do it, then you were a man;
And, to be more than what you were, you would   50
Be so much more the man. Nor time nor place
Did then adhere, and yet you would make both:
They have made themselves, and that their fitness now
Does unmake you. I have given suck, and know
How tender 'tis to love the babe that milks me: 55
I would, while it was smiling in my face,
Have pluck'd my nipple from his boneless gums,
And dash'd the brains out, had I so sworn as you
Have done to this.

MACBETH.   If we should fail?
LADY MACBETH.   We fail!
But screw your courage to the sticking-place,   60
And we'll not fail. When Duncan is asleep—
Whereto the rather shall his day's hard journey
Soundly invite him—his two chamberlains
Will I with wine and wassail so convince
That memory, the warder of the brain,   65
Shall be a fume, and the receipt of reason
A limbeck only: when in swinish sleep
Their drenched natures lie as in a death,
What cannot you and I perform upon
The unguarded Duncan? what not put upon   70
His spongy officers, who shall bear the guilt
Of our great quell?
MACBETH.   Bring forth men-children only;
For thy undaunted mettle should compose
Nothing but males. Will it not be received,
When we have mark'd with blood those sleepy two   75
Of his own chamber and used their very daggers,
That they have done 't?
LADY MACBETH.   Who dares receive it other,
As we shall make our griefs and clamour roar
Upon his death?
MACBETH.   I am settled, and bend up
Each corporal agent to this terrible feat.   80
Away, and mock the time with fairest show:
False face must hide what the false heart doth know. (*Exeunt*)

Macbeth Surrenders to Lady Macbeth   *I.vii.28-82*

*Macbeth, the fearful man of conscience, says no: "We will pro-
ceed no further in this business." Yet Macbeth, the fearless soldier
of courage, gives in to do "this terrible feat." It is his very valor
that makes him vulnerable to Lady Macbeth's derisive taunts of
fear and cowardice. He would, she says, do it if he loved her, and
she would even do it if she were a man; besides, he promised her*

*he would. Against such illicit arguments Macbeth is defenseless,
as are all men who refuse to fight fire with fire.*

By finally daring to do more than "may become a man," Macbeth indeed "is none." He will cease to be a man and become a beast. Ironically enough, this descent to the subhuman is due to trying to ascend to the superhuman. Macbeth is fully honored with "Golden opinions"; but, like the angel Lucifer, he ambitiously wants more, "the golden round" or crown (I.v.29). In the Elizabethan chain of being, man's place in creation is below the angels and above the beasts. "Who dares do more is none." Macbeth dares more and makes himself a beast by trying to be an angel.

Lady Macbeth's brutal image of dashing out her baby's brains shows how thoroughly she has denaturalized herself. Both Macbeth's courage and his daggers are screwed to "the sticking-place," Duncan's heart. In Dante's Inferno *the hypocrites wear golden cloaks of lead to hide their hypocrisy. Likewise, Macbeth now hides the burdensome weight of his hypocrisy under "Golden opinions . . . Which would be worn now in their newest gloss." Macbeth has at last agreed with Lady Macbeth to "look like the innocent flower,/But be the serpent under 't" (I.v.66-67).*

SUMMARY OF ACT I

TEMPTATION IN A MORAL UNIVERSE

Macbeth lives in a world morally arranged into foul and fair, evil and good. As he transgresses the vital boundary between conscience and temptation, he changes and his world changes. These transformations mark the development of the play: its judgmental direction and Macbeth's moral and intellectual state. Macbeth's intellectual quotient (knowing right from wrong) and his moral quotient (doing and willing right or wrong) determine the judgmental direction of his life and the destination of his essential integrity or soul.

Macbeth's abuse of reason and violation of justice can be easily measured. He treacherously welcomes King Duncan—guest, kinsman, and benefactor—in order to murder him and seize the throne. He means to violate the order of succession by overleaping Duncan's eldest son Malcolm, the Prince of Cumberland. He divides himself from his gentle king and unites himself with the witches and his fierce wife.

As Macbeth's will overrules his reason, as "the insane root . . . takes the reason prisoner" (I.iii.84-85), reality changes. First, "Fair is foul, and foul is fair" (I.i.11). The fair Macbeth cannot resist the foul temptation, and the foul Macbeth must now hypocritically appear fair. Second, light must become dark. "Stars, hide your fires;/Let not light see my black and deep desires" (I.iv.50-51). Third, the natural must become unnatural. Lady Macbeth must unsex herself, and Macbeth's heart must go "Against the use of nature" (I.iii.137). Kindness must become cruelty. Fourth, transitory time must become permanent eternity. If Macbeth will "mock the time with fairest show "(I.vii.81), eternity will mock Macbeth "In deepest consequence" (I.iii.126) with "even-handed justice" (I.vii.10). Time takes sides: It is for Macbeth if Macbeth is for Duncan; it is against Macbeth if Macbeth is against Duncan. The "seeds of time" (I.iii.58) are judgmental, the finally eternal.

Between the absolute blackness of the witches and the absolute brightness of Duncan, Macbeth's own world darkens with momentous irony. Macbeth hides the light of the stars and follows the "supernatural soliciting" (I.iii.130) of "The instruments of darkness" (I.iii.124) in the pursuit of "the golden round" (I.v.29). Since Macbeth takes a morally ironic road, his destination will be ironic as well; symbolically, hell instead of heaven. He makes all his values ironic; false appearance is taken for true reality. It is, of course, the temptation of "Vaulting ambition" (I.vii.27) that blinds Macbeth's intellect and perverts his will. Human desire is infinite. The size of the appetite always exceeds the capacity of the stomach. Human desire transcends nature, but nature demands appeasement and gets it. Hence temptation itself is ironic, that is, the freedom to abuse one's freedom and thereby become enslaved. Macbeth consciously knows the inevitable consequences of choosing to defy his judgment and trying to evade "even-handed justice" (I.vii.10). Why, then, does Macbeth trust the false, knowing it is false? Why does he sell eternity for an illusion? Why does this noble man turn monster?

These questions contain the pity and the terror and the mystery of man bewitched.

As a high ranking general who wants to become a higher ranking king, Macbeth becomes drunk with imperial intoxication, ready to rob the world. Indeed, "the charm's wound up" (I.iii.70). Macbeth is going in two directions at once. In climbing up his ambition, he is also going down, descending to "deep damnation" (I.vii.20). Up is down. Fair is foul.

ACT II

Scene I: Court of MACBETH's *castle.*

Enter BANQUO, *and* FLEANCE *bearing a torch before him.*

BANQUO. How goes the night, boy?
FLEANCE. The moon is down; I have not heard the clock.
BANQUO. And she goes down at twelve.
FLEANCE.   I take 't, 'tis later, sir.
BANQUO. Hold, take my sword. There's husbandry in heaven;
Their candles are all out. Take thee that too.   5
A heavy summons lies like lead upon me,
And yet I would not sleep: merciful powers,
Restrain in me the cursed thoughts that nature
Gives way to in repose!

Banquo's Temptation   *II.i.1-9*

The moonless, starless sky sets the stage literally and symbolically for the murder. Night conceals crime, and darkness becomes evil. Banquo suggests the stars ("candles") are out because of heavenly economy ("husbandry"). Demonic abundance is closer to the truth. Earlier, Macbeth's "black and deep desires" had symbolically hidden the stars (I.iv.50). The only survivor in the present scene will be the one bearing a torch in the darkness, Fleance.

It is at night when nature is "in repose" that murderous dreams and anti-nature temptations come (Macbeth repeats this idea later in lines 49-51). Like Macbeth, Banquo himself is tempted by "cursed thoughts," but unlike Macbeth, he calls on "merciful powers" and resists temptations in the night.

(*Enter* MACBETH, *and a* Servant *with a torch*)
Give me my sword.
Who's there?   10
MACBETH. A friend.
BANQUO. What, sir, not yet at rest? The king's a-bed:
He hath been in unusual pleasure, and
Sent forth great largess to your offices.
This diamond he greets your wife withal,   15
By the name of most kind hostess; and shut up
In measureless content.
MACBETH.   Being unprepared,
Our will became the servant to defect;
Which else should free have wrought.
BANQUO.   All's well.
I dreamt last night of the three weird sisters: 20
To you they have show'd some truth.
MACBETH.   I think not of them:
Yet, when we can entreat an hour to serve,
We would spend it in some words upon that business,
If you would grant the time.
BANQUO.   At your kind'st leisure.
MACBETH. If you shall cleave to my consent, when 'tis,   25
It shall make honour for you.
BANQUO.   So I lose none
In seeking to augment it, but still keep
My bosom franchised and allegiance clear,
I shall be counsell'd.
MACBETH.   Good repose the while!
BANQUO. Thanks, sir: the like to you! (*Exeunt* BANQUO *and*
    FLEANCE)   30

Moral Contrast of Banquo and Macbeth   II.i.9-30

Macbeth makes another ironic stage entrance: as the friend of a man he is going to kill. Duncan was deceived by Macbeth earlier (I.iv.14); Banquo will be deceived later. The contrast between Banquo and Macbeth is again underscored. Banquo will do anything for honor, provided he keeps his "bosom franchised and allegiance clear." Macbeth, ironically, will sacrifice conscience and loyalty for honors.

MACBETH. Go bid thy mistress, when my drink is ready,
   She strike upon the bell. Get thee to bed. (*Exit Servant*)
   Is this a dagger which I see before me,
   The handle toward my hand? Come, let me clutch thee.
   I have thee not, and yet I see thee still.   35
   Art thou not, fatal vision, sensible
   To feeling as to sight? or art thou but
   A dagger of the mind, a false creation,
   Proceeding from the heat-oppressed brain?
   I see thee yet, in form as palpable   40
   As this which now I draw.
   Thou marshall'st me the way that I was going;
   And such an instrument I was to use.
   Mine eyes are made the fools o' the other senses,
   Or else worth all the rest; see thee still,   45
   And on thy blade and dudgeon gouts of blood,
   Which was not so before. There's no such thing:
   It is the bloody business which informs
   Thus to mine eyes.

The Dagger Hallucination   II.i.31-49

Long after the murder Lady Macbeth will have her bloody hallucinations (V.i.). Macbeth has hallucinations even before the deed. Is the bloody dagger a "fatal vision" or a "false creation"? Is Macbeth being tempted by illusion or by reality? He is being tempted by an illusion that will become a reality. The dagger in the air is false, just as murder is wrong. Murder is morally unreal until it is done; then it becomes immorally real. Macbeth denies the reality of his illusion. "There's no such thing." Yet in the second half of this soliloquy he goes in search of his "fatal vision."

> Now o'er the one half-world
> Nature seems dead, and wicked dreams abuse 50
> The curtain'd sleep; witchcraft celebrates
> Pale Hecate's offerings, and wither'd murder,
> Alarum'd by his sentinel, the wolf,
> Whose howl's his watch, thus with his stealthy pace,
> With Tarquin's ravishing strides, towards his design 55
> Moves like a ghost.

Macbeth as Tarquin   *II.i.49-56*

As Macbeth goes to do "the bloody business," his thoughts body forth exterior images of his "wicked dreams." Shakespeare artistically uses a secondary image outside the immediate event to express, interpret, and enrich the primary dramatic action. Here the primary action is the departure of Macbeth for Duncan's room in order to commit murder. The secondary images that accompany this murderous exit are "Pale Hecate," the goddess of witchcraft; a personification of "wither'd murder," summoned by "his sentinel, the wolf"; and Tarquin, the Roman ravisher of the chaste Lucrece. The image of the witch Hecate expresses the demonic temptation in Macbeth's exit. The wolf reveals the bestial greed in Macbeth's exit. And "Tarquin's ravishing strides" condemns Macbeth's exit as an act of brutality on innocence (Macbeth is to Tarquin as Duncan is to Lucrece). Thus through secondary images, Shakespeare interprets the primary dramatic action as demonic, bestial, and brutal. Without the imagery we would know the action, but we would not feel the horror of the action nor see either the shape of murder (a wolf) or its heinous magnifications (in Hecate and Tarquin).

> Thou sure and firm-set earth,
> Hear not my steps, which way they walk, for fear
> Thy very stones prate of my whereabout,
> And take the present horror from the time,
> Which now suits with it. Whiles I threat, he lives: 60
> Words to the heat of deeds too cold breath gives. *(A bell rings)*
> I go, and it is done; the bell invites me.
> Hear it not, Duncan; for it is a knell
> That summons thee to heaven or to hell. *(Exit)*

The Bell Summons Macbeth   *II.i.56-64*

As Macbeth steals unsteadily across the "sure and firmset earth," he hears the bell. Lady Macbeth was to "strike upon the bell" when Macbeth's drink was ready (lines 31-32). Realistically, Macbeth steadies his nerve with drink. Symbolically, this drink is the "poisn'd chalice" that "even-handed justice" (I.vii.10-11) ironically commends to Macbeth's own lips.

The final couplet of the scene expresses the embracing irony of the play. Macbeth says the bell is a knell that summons Duncan "to heaven or to hell." Despite his earlier gamble that nothing exists beyond "this bank and shoal of time" (I.vii.6), Macbeth here acknowledges, at least for Duncan, an equivocal future. However, it is not Duncan but Macbeth who is being summoned; not for "thee" but for me does the bell ring. That midnight bell will put Macbeth in the dark forever.

Scene II: The same.

Enter LADY MACBETH.

LADY MACBETH. That which hath made them drunk hath made
>   me bold;
> What hath quench'd them hath given me fire. Hark! Peace!
> It was the owl that shriek'd, the fatal bellman,
> Which gives the stern'st good-night. He is about it:
> The doors are open; and the surfeited grooms   5
> Do mock their charge with snores: I have drugg'd their possets,
> That death and nature do contend about them,

Whether they live or die.

MACBETH (*within*). Who's there? what, ho!

LADY MACBETH. Alack, I am afraid they have awaked,   10
And 'tis not done. The attempt and not the deed
Confounds us. Hark! I laid their daggers ready;
He could not miss 'em. Had he not resembled
My father as he slept, I had done 't.

(*Enter* MACBETH)

                                        My husband!

MACBETH. I have done the deed. Didst thou not hear a noise?   15

LADY MACBETH. I heard the owl scream and the crickets cry.
Did not you speak?

MACBETH.   When?

LADY MACBETH.   Now.

MACBETH.   As I descended?

LADY MACBETH. Ay.

MACBETH. Hark!
Who lies i' the second chamber?

LADY MACBETH.   Donalbain.   20

MACBETH. This is a sorry sight. (*Looking on his hands*)

LADY MACBETH. A foolish thought, to say a sorry sight.

MACBETH. There's one did laugh in 's sleep, and one cried
    "Murder!"
That they did wake each other: I stood and heard them:
But they did say their prayers, and address'd them   25
Again to sleep.

LADY MACBETH. There are two lodged together.

MACBETH. One cried "God bless us!" and "Amen" the other;
As they had seen me with these hangman's hands.
Listening their fear, I could not say "Amen,"
When they did say "God bless us!"

LADY MACBETH   Consider it not so deeply.   30

MACBETH. But wherefore could not I pronounced "Amen"?
I had most need of blessing, and "Amen"
Stuck in my throat.

LADY MACBETH.   These deeds must not be thought
After these ways; so, it will make us mad.

MACBETH. Methought I heard a voice cry "Sleep no more!   35

Macbeth does murder sleep," the innocent sleep,
Sleep that knits up the ravell'd sleave of care,
The death of each day's life, sore labour's bath,
Balm of hurt minds, great nature's second course,
Chief nourisher in life's feast,—

LADY MACBETH.   What do you mean?   40

MACBETH. Still it cried "Sleep no more!" to all the house:
"Glamis hath murder'd sleep, and therefore Cawdor
Shall sleep no more; Macbeth shall sleep no more."

LADY MACBETH. Who was it that thus cried? Why, worthy thane,
You do unbend your noble strength, to think   45
So brainsickly of things. Go get some water,
And wash this filthy witness from your hand.
Why did you bring these daggers from the place?
They must lie there: go carry them; and smear
The sleepy grooms with blood.

MACBETH.   I'll go no more: 50
I am afraid to think what I have done;
Look on 't again I dare not.

LADY MACBETH.   Infirm of purpose!
Give me the daggers: the sleeping and the dead
Are but as pictures: 'tis the eye of childhood
That fears a painted devil. If he do bleed,   55
I'll gild the faces of the grooms withal;
For it must seem their guilt. *(Exit. Knocking within)*

MACBETH.   Whence is that knocking?
How is 't with me, when every noise appals me?
What hands are here? ha! they pluck out mine eyes.
Will all great Neptune's ocean wash this blood   60
Clean from my hand? No, this my hand will rather
The multitudinous seas incarnadine,
Making the green one red.

(Re-enter LADY MACBETH)

LADY MACBETH. My hands are of your colour; but I shame
To wear a heart so white. *(Knocking within)* I hear a knock-
    ing   65
At the south entry: retire we to our chamber:
A little water clears us of this deed:

How easy is it, then! Your constancy
Hath left you unattended. (*Knocking within*) Hark! more
  knocking.
Get on your nightgown, lest occasion call us,   70
And show us to be watchers. Be not lost
So poorly in your thoughts.
MACBETH. To know my deed, 'twere best not know myself.
  (*Knocking within*)
Wake Duncan with thy knocking! I would thou couldst!
  (*Exeunt*)

Macbeth Murders Duncan   *II.ii.1-74*

*The moral sensitivity of Macbeth and Lady Macbeth is re-
vealed immediately after the murder. Unlike his wife, Macbeth
is transfixed by the enormity of his crime. He finds himself in a
dark world newly lighted by terror, by such terrors as appalling
noises, inarticulate Amen's, eternal insomnia, a discolored ocean,
self-horror, and infinite regret. Although Lady Macbeth tells
Macbeth to "Consider it not so deeply," the "deepest consequence" (I.iii.126) of murder begins and cannot be trammeled up.
His hands no longer seem to be his own hands. Blood has made
them strangers, and as a murderer he has become a stranger to
himself. "To know my deed, 'twere best not know myself."*

*The noble Macbeth has discovered his alter ego, the evil
Macbeth. Split from himself, Macbeth discovers himself. The
penalty for such complete self-knowledge is paralyzing horror.
Evil is no longer an illusion, a phantom dagger. It is real, a
bloody dagger. So real is Macbeth's dagger that it cuts him off
from God when he cuts Duncan off from life. Macbeth can no
longer say "Amen," the solemn affirmation of God's will. Indeed,
Macbeth can hardly be expected to affirm a power that must
now negate him.*

*Shakespeare amplifies the dimensions of Macbeth's crime
chiefly through nature imagery. Nature is not merely naturalistic
(the power of growth and decay); it is sacramental; that is, it is
the bearer of a transcendent power, the power of "deepest consequence (I.iii.126) and "deep damnation" (I.vii.20). Nature par-*

ticipates in the crime and suffers; a crime against man is a crime against nature. When Macbeth kills Duncan in his sleep, Macbeth kills "innocent sleep" itself, "great nature's second course." In murdering Duncan Macbeth "hath murder'd sleep" and "Macbeth shall sleep no more." Again, in a superb hyperbole, the agonized Macbeth imagines what will happen when he tries to wash the blood from his hands. Water, instead of washing off the blood, becomes bloody itself. A crime against Duncan is a crime against "great Neptune's ocean," turning "the green one red." Here is expressed the original theme of the play: fair is foul, green is red.

As a symbol, water has a double sacramental possibility. It can refuse to wash, as it were, and suffer Macbeth's crime, or it can wash and thereby pardon Macbeth's crime. But only "by the grace of Grace" (V.viii.72) does water purify the repentant. So long as Macbeth refuses repentance, water discolors and "suffers" along with the rest of nature. Were the nature imagery non-sacramental, Macbeth's bloody hands would never turn the green ocean red.

Unlike her terrified husband, Lady Macbeth remains surgically cold-blooded. She boldly returns the bloody daggers, smears the grooms with blood, and tells Macbeth that "A little water clears us of this deed." It is as easy to wash one's conscience as one's hands. She further tells Macbeth to forget the murder or else "it will make us mad." This becomes a prophetic line for Lady Macbeth, who will eventually go mad herself despite her ruthless amnesia. The only touch of humanity left her is the memory of her father which prevents her from doing the deed herself.

The contrast between Macbeth and Lady Macbeth has clearly emerged. Macbeth's blood leaves his heart when his hands turn red; Lady Macbeth is shamed "To wear a heart so white." Lady Macbeth's nerves are frozen, but the ice will eventually shatter. On the other hand, Macbeth's nerves are immediately shattered, but eventually they will become numbed.

Scene III: *The same.*

Knocking within. Enter a Porter.

PORTER. Here 's a knocking indeed! If a man were porter of hell-

gate, he should have old turning the key. (*Knocking within*)
Knock, knock, knock! Who's there, i' the name of Beelzebub?
Here 's a farmer, that hanged himself on the expectation of
plenty: come in time; have napkins enow about you; here you'll
sweat for 't. (*Knocking within*) Knock, knock! Who 's there, in
the other devil's name? Faith, here's an equivocator, that
could swear in both the scales against either scale; who committed treason enough for God's sake, yet could not equivocate
to heaven: O, come in, equivocator. (*Knocking within*) Knock,
knock, knock! Who 's there? Faith, here 's an English tailor
come hither, for stealing out of a French hose: come in, tailor;
here you may roast your goose. (*Knocking within*) Knock,
knock; never at quiet! What are you? But this place is too cold
for hell. I'll devil-porter it no further: I had thought to have
let in some of all professions that go the primrose way to the
everlasting bonfire. (*Knocking within*) Anon, anon! I pray you,
remember the porter. (*Opens the gate*)

The Porter of Hell   *II.iii.1-26*

*Before the murder Macbeth's castle was a place where
"heaven's breath/Smells wooingly" (I.vi.5-6). After the murder,
however, this heaven has become hell, as suggested by the present references to "hell-gate," "Beelzebub," the other devil's name"
(perhaps Satan but eventually Macbeth himself), "too cold for
hell," and "the everlasting bonfire." The purpose of this scene
(apart from De Quincey's fantasy and Coleridge's disgust) is not
mere comic relief; it is rather symbolic geography. Just as the
ocean turned from green to red, so Macbeth's world changed
from heaven to hell. Again, fair is foul. Those who enter Macbeth's gate, enter, symbolically, hell, the world of self-willed
violence and treachery. The porter ironically says that "this place
is too cold for hell." Yet traitors to kinsmen, countrymen, guests,
and benefactors are, in the tradition of Dante, embedded in ice.
The porter's description of "An equivocator . . . who committed
treason enough for God's sake, yet could not equivocate to
heaven" is a description of Macbeth's peril. It takes a drunken
porter to tell the sober truth.*

(*Enter* MACDUFF *and* LENNOX)

MACDUFF. Was it so late, friend, ere you went to bed,
That you do lie so late?

PORTER. 'Faith, sir, we were carousing till the second cock: and
drink, sir, is a great provoker of three things.

MACDUFF. What three things does drink especially provoke?   30

PORTER. Marry, sir, nose-painting, sleep, and urine. Lechery, sir,
it provokes, and unprovokes; it provokes the desire, but it takes
away the performance: therefore, much drink may be said to
be an equivocator with lechery: it makes him, and it mars him;
it sets him on, and it takes him off; it persuades him, and disheartens him; makes him stand to, and not stand to; in conclusion, equivocates him in a sleep, and, giving him the lie,
leaves him.   40

MACDUFF. I believe drink gave thee the lie last night.

PORTER. That it did, sir, i' the very throat on me: but I requited
him for his lie; and, I think, being too strong for him, though
he took up my legs sometime, yet I made a shift to cast him.

MACDUFF. Is thy master stirring?

On Equivocation   *II.iii.26-46*

*Like the porter's drunken lecher, Macbeth is the witches'
drunken climber. The witches are the real equivocators, deceiving Macbeth with their ambiguous knowledge (especially later in
IV.i), saying one thing and meaning another, making foul appear
fair. Throughout the play Macbeth follows the lecher's pattern
whose drink "sets him on, and takes him off; it persuades him,
and disheartens him. . . ." Drink provokes unequivocal equivocation, and Macbeth is drunk with ambition.*

(*Enter* MACBETH.)

Our knocking has awaked him; here he comes.

LENNOX. Good morrow, noble sir.

MACBETH.   Good morrow, both.

MACDUFF. Is the king stirring, worthy thane?

MACBETH.   Not yet.   50

MACDUFF. He did command me to call timely on him:
  I have almost slipp'd the hour.
MACBETH.   I'll bring you to him.
MACDUFF. I know this is a joyful trouble to you;
  But yet 'tis one.
MACBETH. The labour we delight in physics pain.   55
  This is the door.
MACDUFF.   I'll make so bold to call,
  For 'tis my limited service. (*Exit*)
LENNOX. Goes the king hence to-day?
MACBETH.   He does: he did appoint so.
LENNOX. The night has been unruly: where we lay,
  Our chimneys were blown down; and, as they say,   60
  Lamentings heard i' the air; strange screams of death,
  And prophesying with accents terrible
  Of dire combustion and confused events
  New hatch'd to the woeful time: the obscure bird
  Clamour'd the livelong night: some say, the earth   65
  Was feverous and did shake.
MACBETH.   'Twas a rough night.
LENNOX. My young remembrance cannot parallel
  A fellow to it.

Earthquake after the Murder   *II.iii.47-67*

  *The reason for the "rough night" is Duncan's murder. The
cause and effect between man and nature expresses the symbolic
dimension of Macbeth's deed. When the fair Macbeth turns foul,
fair weather also turns foul. A violent image of nature that is
suffering Macbeth's unnatural crime contrasts here with an
earlier image of nature. Before the murder Macbeth walked on
the "sure and firm-set earth" (II.i.56). After the deed "the earth/
Was feverous and did shake." Shakespeare's compassionate geography is not so much the pathetic fallacy of personifying
nature; rather, nature is symbolically conceived as part of man's
history and the universe. What happens to man happens to nature and the universe.*

(*Re-enter* MACDUFF)

MACDUFF. O horror, horror horror! Tongue nor heart
Cannot conceive nor name thee!

MACBETH. ⎱
LENNOX. ⎰   What's the matter?   70

MACDUFF. Confusion now hath made his masterpiece!
Most sacrilegious murder hath broke ope
The Lord's anointed temple, and stole thence
The life o' the building!

MACBETH.   What is 't you say? the life?

LENNOX. Mean you his majesty?   75

MACDUFF. Approach the chamber, and destroy your sight
With a new Gorgon: do not bid me speak;
See, and then speak yourselves. (*Exeunt* MACBETH *and* LENNOX)
                              Awake, awake!
Ring the alarum-bell. Murder and treason!
Banquo and Donalbain! Malcolm! awake!   80
Shake off this downy sleep, death's counterfeit,
And look on death itself! up, up, and see
The great doom's image! Malcolm! Banquo!
As from your graves rise up, and walk like sprites,
To countenance this horror! Ring the bell. (*Bell rings*)   85

The Murder Discovered   *II.iii.67-85*

Macduff describes the "Murder and treason" with classical and Christian allusions. The sight of the horror is likened to "a new Gorgon," that is, a sight so hideous that it would turn the beholder to stone and drive him to despair. In Christian terms, "Most sacrilegious murder hath broke ope/The Lord's anointed temple." Here the murder of Duncan, "a most sainted king" (IV.iii.109), is symbolically interpreted as a crucifixion, fulfilling the much earlier allusion in the play to "Golgotha" (I.ii.40), the "place of the skull" where Christ was crucified. Duncan's murder is seen as a divine murder, not only because of the dogma of the divine right of kings, but also because of Duncan's Christ-like purity and innocence.

If the Christian allusion interprets the murder as the cruci-

fixion of a divine man, the classical allusion interprets it as a triple horror without divinity. "O horror, horror, horror!" cries Macduff. However, the hated Medusa, one of the three horrible Gorgons in classical mythology, is beheaded by the hero Perseus with the help of divine aid. As Perseus, with the goddess Athene's guidance, cut off Medusa's head, so Macduff, "with Him above/To ratify the work" (III.vi.32-33), will cut off the head of Macbeth, the creator of the horrible murder of Duncan.

The Christian allusion reveals a divine victim; the classical allusion, a divine avenger. In the Christian context divinity (Duncan) is powerless; in the classical context divinity (Macduff) is powerful. Both allusions reveal the sacred dimension of secular events.

(*Enter* LADY MACBETH)

LADY MACBETH. What's the business,
    That such a hideous trumpet calls to parley
    The sleepers of the house? speak, speak!

MACDUFF.   O gentle lady,
    'Tis not for you to hear what I can speak:
    The repetition, in a woman's ear,   90
    Would murder as it fell.

(*Enter* BANQUO)
                                    O Banquo, Banquo,
    Our royal master's murder'd!

LADY MACBETH.   Woe, alas!
    What, in our house?

BANQUO.   Too cruel any where.
    Dear Duff, I prithee, contradict thyself,
    And say it is not so.   95

(*Re-enter* MACBETH *and* LENNOX, *with* ROSS)

MACBETH. Had I but died an hour before this chance,
    I had lived a blessed time; for, from this instant,
    There's nothing serious in mortality:
    All is but toys: renown and grace is dead;
    The wine of life is drawn, and the mere lees   100
    Is left this vault to brag of.

Macbeth's Instant of Recognition   *II.iii.86-101*

Lady Macbeth's prepared reaction to the murder is transparent hypocrisy; Macbeth's is ironic hypocrisy. He equivocates to his listeners and to himself. Macbeth's desire to die before Duncan sounds like supreme devotion to Duncan; actually it is supreme sorrow for himself. Had Duncan died a natural death, Macbeth indeed would have "lived a blessed time." However, because Macbeth murdered Duncan, "from this instant,/There's nothing serious in mortality." Instead of being blessed, the time is cursed and damned. "All is but toys: renown and grace is dead." Macbeth's world is suddenly robbed of all value. He no longer has to lock his doors. The gates of hell are open, but the gates of heaven are guarded. No one wants to rob hell.

The importance of timing is stressed. Had Macbeth died but "an hour before this chance," he "had lived a blessed time." If Macbeth misses blessedness by an hour, he meets emptiness in an instant. In one instant, the moment of murder, Macbeth's entire life hereafter is lighted by darkness and heated by coldness. All values are transvalued. In the tradition of Dante, our present life determines our life hereafter (status animarum post mortem). Macbeth does not have to wait until he dies to go to hell. His hell begins the moment he challenges "even-handed justice" and murders Duncan. Eternity is in time because the consequences of the instant are forever. Ironically, the "deepest consequence" (I.iii.126) is that life becomes inconsequential. "All is but toys."

(*Enter* MALCOLM *and* DONALBAIN)

DONALBAIN. What is amiss?

MACBETH.   You are, and do not know 't:
 The spring, the head, the fountain of your blood
 Is stopp'd; the very source of it is stopp'd.

MACDUFF. Your royal father's murdered.

MALCOLM.   O, by whom?   105

LENNOX. Those of his chamber, as it seem'd, had done 't:
 Their hands and faces were all badged with blood;
 So were their daggers, which unwiped we found

Upon their pillows:
They stared, and were distracted; no man's life   110
Was to be trusted with them.
MACBETH. O, yet I do repent me of my fury,
   That I did kill them.
MACDUFF.   Wherefore did you so?
MACBETH. Who can be wise, amazed, temperate and furious,
   Loyal and neutral, in a moment? No man: 115
   The expedition of my violent love
   Outrun the pauser, reason. Here lay Duncan,
   His silver skin laced with his golden blood;
   And his gash'd stabs look'd like a breach in nature
   For ruin's wasteful entrance: there, the murderers,   120
   Steep'd in the colours of their trade, their daggers
   Unmannerly breech'd with gore: who could refrain,
   That had a heart to love, and in that heart
   Courage to make 's love known?
LADY MACBETH.   Help me hence, ho!
MACDUFF. Look to the lady.
MALCOLM   (*aside to* DONALBAIN). Why do we hold our
   tongues,   125
   That most may claim this argument for ours?
DONALBAIN (*aside to* MALCOLM). What should be spoken here,
   where our fate,
   Hid in an auger-hole, may rush, and seize us?
   Let's away;
   Our tears are not yet brew'd.
MALCOLM   (*aside to* DONALBAIN). Nor our strong
   sorrow   130
   Upon the foot of motion.
BANQUO.   Look to the lady: (LADY MACBETH *is
   carried out*)
   And when we have our naked frailties hid,
   That suffer in exposure, let us meet,
   And question this most bloody piece of work,
   To know it further. Fears and scruples shake us: 135
   In the great hand of God I stand; and thence

Against the undivulged pretence I fight
Of treasonous malice.

MACDUFF.   And so do I.

ALL.   So all.

MACBETH. Let's briefly put on manly readiness,
And meet i' the hall together.

ALL.   Well contented.   140

                    (Exeunt all but MALCOLM *and*
                       DONALBAIN)

MALCOLM. What will you do? Let's not consort with them:
To show an unfelt sorrow is an office
Which the false man does easy. I'll to England.

DONALBAIN. To Ireland, I; our separated fortune
Shall keep us both the safer: where we are,   145
There's daggers in men's smiles: the near in blood,
The nearer bloody.

MALCOLM.   This murderous shaft that's shot
Hath not yet lighted, and our safest way
Is to avoid the aim. Therefore, to horse;
And let us not be dainty of leave-taking,   150
But shift away: there's warrant in that theft
Which steals itself, when there's no mercy left. *(Exeunt)*

Malcolm and Donalbain Escape   *II.iii.102-152*

*Foul continues to appear fair. Lady Macbeth pretends to faint;
to think otherwise is to be naive. Macbeth kills the grooms pre-
tending to punish Duncan's murderers in a fit of revengeful fury.
He claims his "violent love" outran "the pauser, reason." Actually,
his violent selflove outran his restraining reason when he murdered Duncan. The innocent grooms, earlier smeared with blood
by Lady Macbeth, appeared guilty. Fair appeared foul. Their
innocence cannot now be discovered; dead men tell no tales. For
fear of their own lives, Duncan's sons, Malcolm and Donalbain,
escape. "There's daggers in men's smiles: the near in blood,/
The nearer bloody." Again fair appears foul; the sons become
suspect of murdering their father. Untainted with suspicion is
Banquo, who stands "In the great hand of God."*
The many references to blood, especially "golden blood," sug-

gest sacrifice. Not being in the normal spectrum, gold (as opposed to natural yellow) expresses a transcendence over nature, in this case, the divinity of kings. At the same time, Duncan's "gash'd stabs look'd like a breach in nature." Symbolically, the crime against King Duncan is a crime against nature and the supernatural.

Scene IV: Outside MACBETH'S *castle.*

Enter ROSS *and an* old Man.

OLD MAN. Threescore and ten I can remember well:
   Within the volume of which time I have seen
   Hours dreadful and things strange; but this sore night
   Hath trifled former knowings.
ROSS.   Ah, good father,   5
   Thou seest, the heavens, as troubled with man's act,
   Threaten his bloody stage: by the clock, 'tis day,
   And yet dark night strangles the travelling lamp:
   Is 't night's predominance, or the day's shame,
   That darkness does the face of earth entomb,
   When living light should kiss it?
OLD MAN.   'Tis unnatural   10
   Even like the deed that's done. On Tuesday last,
   A falcon, towering in her pride of place,
   Was by a mousing owl hawk'd at and kill'd.
ROSS. And Duncan's horses—a thing most strange and certain—
   Beauteous and swift, the minions of their race,   15
   Turn'd wild in nature, broke their stalls, flung out,
   Contending 'gainst obedience, as they would make
   War with mankind.
OLD MAN.   'Tis said they eat each other.
ROSS. They did so, to the amazement of mine eyes
   That look'd upon 't. Here comes the good Macduff.   20
(*Enter* MACDUFF)
   How goes the world, sir, now?
MACDUFF.   Why, see you not?
ROSS. Is 't known who did this more than bloody deed?
MACDUFF. Those that Macbeth hath slain.
ROSS.   Alas, the day!

What good could they pretend?

MACDUFF.   They were suborn'd:
Malcolm and Donalbain, the king's two sons,   25
Are stol'n away and fled; which puts upon them
Suspicion of the deed.

ROSS.   'Gainst nature still!
Thriftless ambition, that wilt ravin up
Thine own life's means! Then 'tis most like
The sovereignty will fall upon Macbeth.   30

MACDUFF. He is already named, and gone to Scone
To be invested.

ROSS.   Where is Duncan's body?

MACDUFF. Carried to Colmekill,
The sacred storehouse of his predecessors,
And guardian of their bones.

ROSS.   Will you to Scone?   35

MACDUFF. No, cousin, I'll to Fife.

ROSS.   Well, I will thither.

MACDUFF. Well, may you see things well done there: adieu!
Lest our old robes sit easier than our new!

ROSS. Farewell, father.

OLD MAN. God's benison go with you; and with those   40
That would make good of bad, and friends of foes! (*Exeunt*)

Outraged Cosmos   *II.iv*

*Murder has unexpected magnitudes. In imagery of heaven and
earth, of darkness and of light, and birds and beasts, these magnitudes are fully revealed. The primary event of Macbeth's horrid
deed creates the secondary image of cosmic consequence. Here
"thou seest, the heavens, as troubled with man's act,/Threaten his
bloody stage [i.e., the world]." Macbeth lives in a cosmic setting;
that is, he lives in an interdependent world and universe where
nature is sacramental, not neutral; where the cosmos is concerned
with, not indifferent to, "man's act." The whole course of nature
is disrupted. The sun itself does not rise and shine. When Macbeth kills Duncan, king of the microcosm of Scotland, he also
kills the sun, likewise king of the macrocosm of planets. Mac-*

beth's crime against Duncan is a crime against the sun, the symbol of life (heat) and knowledge (light). Macbeth makes his life sterile and meaningless because he, in effect, murders the sun. The symbolic death of the sun represents not only the "night's predominance" or evil, but also "the day's shame," that is, nature's disgrace at Duncan's unnatural murder. "'Tis unnatural, Even like the deed that's done," says the Old Man, almost a personification of time himself.

Macbeth murders the powerful sun only when he first murders the powerless Duncan ("a most sainted king," IV.iii.109). Such is the paradox of earthly and divine powers. The meek King Duncan is so powerful that his death can "the earth entomb." Indeed "another Golgotha" (I.ii.40), another crucifixion, a cosmic coronary, as it were.

Even animal nature participates in the crime. An owl, which feeds on mice, attacks a powerful falcon. Small animals normally do not attack larger animals unless the smaller are crazed by rabies. The chain of being is violently reversed: the lower orders attack the superior orders, just as the crazed Macbeth turned against Duncan. Such radical disorder results in self-destruction. Duncan's trained horses, "Turn'd wild in nature . . . as they would make/War with mankind," at last "eat each other."

Here is a universe amassing the moral outrages of Macbeth until the sun itself is extinguished in the cosmic storm. Indeed, "the heavens, as troubled with man's act,/Threaten his bloody stage." The picture of Scotland's bad weather is painted by Macbeth.

SUMMARY OF ACT II

THE MURDER MAGNIFIED

The relationship between deed and consequence becomes apocalyptic. One murder, murders the universe. Scotland suddenly becomes colossal, a map of the world; the microcosm usurps the macrocosm. Macbeth's deed is life-sized, but it is magnified in cosmos-sized imagery. When Macbeth murders Duncan he murders "innocent sleep" (II.ii.36); he makes "the multitudinous seas incarnadine" (II.ii.62); he makes his castle a freezing hell; he breaks open "The Lord's anointed temple" (II.iii.73); he instantly renders "nothing serious in mortality" (II.iii.98); and he strangles the sun so that "darkness does the face of earth entomb" (I.iv.9). These magnified images prove that a regicide is not merely a regicide; it is also a geocide, even a biocide. The earth and life itself are being murdered.

The consequences of the murder are magnified for various reasons. First, the crime is a violation against the social hierarchy and the chain of authority; a rebellious subject kills a just king, a king with divine right on his side. Second, Macbeth not only kills his king, but at the same time kills his kinsman, guest, and benefactor. Third, without the enlarged consequences and the radical reactions of nature, the true face and horror of the murder would not be apparent. Unnatural images are necessary to reveal the ugliness of evil. No wonder Macbeth says, "I am afraid to think what I have done;/Look on 't again I dare not." (II.ii.51-52). Indeed it does "destroy your sight/With a new Gorgon" (II.iii.76-77). Hell must be seen to be known. Fourth, the natural world reflects the moral world because man's state in nature depends on more than nature. The violent reaction of nature reveals to Macbeth that he lives not completely in nature. He also lives by "even-handed justice" (I.vii.10). In fact, the foundation of nature itself rests in the scales of justice. When the scales are balanced, as before the murder, the earth was "sure and firmset" (II.i.56). But when the scales are unbalanced by "Most sacrilegious murder" (II.iii.72), "the earth/Was feverous and did shake" (II.iii.65-66). Both the state of nature and the state of man depend on the untrammeled scales of "even-handed justice." When fair Macbeth becomes foul, fair nature becomes foul as well. His deed destroys sleep, discolors water, entombs the earth, and strangles the sun.

Ambition, treachery, and violence win Macbeth the coveted crown, but at the same time he loses "innocent sleep" (I.ii.36). Macbeth is sticky with blood and damnation, for he lives in a universe whose "heavens, as troubled with man's act,/Threaten his bloody stage" (II.iv.5-6). As finally magnified, the imagery of nature and the cosmos becomes a moral seismograph of Macbeth's bloody deed.

ACT III

Scene I: *Forres. The palace.*

Enter BANQUO.

BANQUO. Thou hast it now: king, Cawdor, Glamis, all,
As the weird women promised, and, I fear,
Thou play'dst most foully for 't: yet it was said
It should not stand in thy posterity,
But that myself should be the root and father   5
Of many kings. If there come truth from them—
As upon thee, Macbeth, their speeches shine—
Why, by the verities on thee made good,
May they not be my oracles as well,
And set me up in hope? But hush! no more.   10

(*Sennet sounded. Enter* MACBETH, *as king,* LADY MACBETH, *as queen,* LENNOX, ROSS, Lords, Ladies, *and* Attendants)

MACBETH. Here's our chief guest.

LADY MACBETH.   If he had been forgotten.
It had been as a gap in our great feast,
And all-thing unbecoming.

MACBETH. To-night we hold a solemn supper, sir,
And I'll request your presence.

BANQUO.   Let your highness   15
Command upon me; to the which my duties
Are with a most indissoluble tie
For ever knit.

MACBETH. Ride you this afternoon?

BANQUO. Ay, my good lord.   20

MACBETH. We should have else desired your good advice,
Which still hath been both grave and prosperous,
In this day's council; but we'll take to-morrow.
Is 't far you ride?

BANQUO. As far, my lord, as will fill up the time   25
'Twixt this and supper: go not my horse the better,
I must become a borrower of the night
For a dark hour or twain.

MACBETH.   Fail not our feast.

BANQUO. My lord, I will not.

MACBETH. We hear, our bloody cousins are bestow'd   30
  In England and in Ireland, not confessing
  Their cruel parricide, filling their hearers
  With strange invention: but of that to-morrow,
  When therewithal we shall have cause of state
  Craving us jointly. Hie you to horse: adieu,   35
  Till you return at night. Goes Fleance with you?
BANQUO. Ay, my good lord: our time does call upon's.
MACBETH. I wish your horses swift and sure of foot;
  And so I do commend you to their backs.
  Farewell. (*Exit* BANQUO)   40
  Let every man be master of his time
  Till seven at night: to make society
  The sweeter welcome, we will keep ourself
  Till supper-time alone: while then, God be with you!
          (*Exeunt all but* MACBETH, *and an Attendant*)
  Sirrah, a word with you: attend those men   45
  Our pleasure?
ATTENDANT. They are, my lord, without the palace gate.
MACBETH. Bring them before us. (*Exit Attendant*)

Banquo's Invitation to Supper   *III.i.1-48*

*Banquo suspects Macbeth of foul play but cannot prove his
suspicions. However, Banquo does not suspect Macbeth far
enough. Macbeth, as the rest of this scene reveals, has even more
murder on his mind when he invites Banquo to "a solemn supper." A double irony is anticipated. When Macbeth says, "Fail
not our feast," he is really not expecting Banquo to attend because he hopes to have him murdered by suppertime. More
ironic, when Banquo replies to the invitation, "My lord, I will
not," he does not suspect he will be murdered. Yet his promise
is prophetic. Actually, he will not fail the feast. He will attend
as a ghost, albeit a rather undernourished ghost (III.iv).*

          To be thus is nothing;
  But to be safely thus.—Our fears in Banquo
  Stick deep; and in his royalty of nature   50

Reigns that which would be fear'd: 'tis much he dares;
And, to that dauntless temper of his mind,
He hath a wisdom that doth guide his valour
To act in safety. There is none but he
Whose being I do fear: and, under him,   55
My Genius is rebuked; as, it is said,
Mark Antony's was by Caesar. He chid the sisters
When first they put the name of king upon me,
And bade them speak to him: then prophet-like
They hail'd him father to a line of kings: 60
Upon my head they placed a fruitless crown,
And put a barren sceptre in my gripe,
Thence to be wrench'd with an unlineal hand,
No son of mine succeeding. If 't be so,
For Banquo's issue have I filed my mind;   65
For them the gracious Duncan have I murder'd;
Put rancours in the vessel of my peace
Only for them; and mine eternal jewel
Given to the common enemy of man,
To make them kings, the seed of Banquo kings!   70
Rather than so, come fate into the list,
And champion me to the utterance! Who's there?

Macbeth's Fear of Banquo   *III.i.48-72*

*Macbeth not only wants the crown; he wants a fruitful crown,
a crown not only for himself but for his descendents. Not merely
the present but also the future is needed to satisfy Macbeth's
"Vaulting ambition" (I.vii.27). In short, Macbeth wants a kind
of immortality. The present is not enough; he must also possess
the future. Time is not enough; he must also possess eternity.
However, in trying to cheat time by murdering Banquo and
Fleance, eternity becomes a menace to Macbeth. Although Macbeth fears Banquo, it is Macbeth's soul—"mine eternal jewel"—
that is really in jeopardy.*

*With an enlightened desperation, Macbeth begins to recognize
his folly. Indeed, he has gained "a fruitless crown" and "a barren*

sceptre." He has defiled his mind and has thrown away his "eternal jewel," given it to "the common enemy of man" (the devil) and ironically has become himself "the common enemy of man." He has futilely murdered "the gracious Duncan." The fair crown has brought foul consequences. Macbeth gains neither worldly nor otherworldly security. He fears Banquo alive; later he will fear him dead.

(*Re-enter* Attendant, *with two* Murderers)

    Now go to the door, and stay there till we call. (*Exit Attendant*)

    Was it not yesterday we spoke together?

FIRST MURDERER. It was, so please your highness.

MACBETH.   Well, then, now   75

    Have you consider'd of my speeches? Know

    That it was he in the times past which held you

    So under fortune, which you thought had been

    Our innocent self: this I made good to you

    In our last conference, pass'd in probation with you,   80

    How you were borne in hand, how cross'd, the instruments,

    Who wrought with them, and all things else that might

    To half a soul and to a notion crazed

    Say "Thus did Banquo."

FIRST MURDERER.   You made it known to us.

MACBETH. I did so, and went further, which is now   85

    Our point of second meeting. Do you find

    Your patience so predominant in your nature

    That you can let this go? Are you so gospell'd

    To pray for this good man and for his issue,

    Whose heavy hand hath bow'd you to the grave   90

    And beggar'd yours for ever?

FIRST MURDERER.   We are men, my liege.

MACBETH. Ay, in the catalogue ye go for men;

    As hounds and greyhounds, mongrels, spaniels, curs,

    Shoughs, water-rugs and demi-wolves are clept

    All by the name of dogs: the valued file   95

Distinguishes the swift, the slow, the subtle,
The housekeeper, the hunter, every one
According to the gift which bounteous nature
Hath in him closed, whereby he does receive
Particular addition, from the bill   100
That writes them all alike: and so of men.
Now, if you have a station in the file,
Not i' the worst rank of manhood, say 't;
And I will put that business in your bosoms,
Whose execution takes your enemy off,   105
Grapples you to the heart and love of us,
Who wear our health but sickly in his life,
Which in his death were perfect.
SECOND MURDERER.   I am one, my liege,
Whom the vile blows and buffets of the world
Have so incensed that I am reckless what   110
I do to spite the world.
FIRST MURDERER.   And I another
So weary with disasters, tugg'd with fortune,
That I would set my life on any chance,
To mend it, or be rid on 't.
MACBETH.   Both of you
Know Banquo was your enemy.
BOTH MURDERERS.   True, my lord.   115
MACBETH. So is he mine; and in such bloody distance,
That every minute of his being thrusts
Against my near'st of life: and though I could
With barefaced power sweep him from my sight
And bid my will avouch it, yet I must not,   120
For certain friends that are both his and mine,
Whose loves I may not drop, but wail his fall
Who I myself struck down; and thence it is,
That I to your assistance do make love,
Masking the business from the common eye   125
For sundry weighty reasons.
SECOND MURDERER.   We shall, my lord,
Performed what you command us.
FIRST MURDERER.   Though our lives—

MACBETH. Your spirits shine through you. Within this hour at
  most
  I will advise you where to plant yourselves;
  Acquaint you with the perfect spy o' the time,   130
  The moment on 't; for 't must be done to-night,
  And something from the palace; always thought
  That I require a clearness: and with him—
  To leave no rubs nor botches in the work—
  Fleance his son, that keeps him company,   135
  Whose absence is no less material to me
  Than is his father's, must embrace the fate
  Of that dark hour. Resolve yourselves apart:
  I'll come to you anon.
BOTH MURDERERS.   We are resolved, my lord.
MACBETH. I'll call upon you straight: abide within. (*Exeunt
  Murderers*)   140
  It is concluded. Banquo, thy soul's flight,
  If it find heaven, must find it out to-night. (*Exit*)

Macbeth Hires Murderers   *III.i.73-142*

*This interview with the murderers communicates from two
angles at once. First, it makes a direct, literal statement. Macbeth
persuades and hires the murderers to kill Banquo. Although Macbeth tells the reckless murderers why they themselves should
want to kill Banquo (to redress old wrongs alleged to Banquo),
Macbeth never tells his hirelings why he personallly wants
Banquo and Fleance dead (to insure permanent possession of
the crown). Second, there is an oblique, ironic statement. In
hiring the murderers Macbeth becomes a demonic tempter, com-
parable to his wife. In describing Banquo's "heavy hand," Macbeth describes himself. In comparing the varieties of men to
varieties of dogs, Macbeth betrays his own bestial nature and
treatment of humanity. The reckless, weary despair expressed
by the two murderers expresses Macbeth's later world-weariness
(V.ii and V.v). Not only is Macbeth's future anticipated, but his
past is repeated. Before murdering Duncan, Macbeth had said
that the tolling bell was "a knell/That summons thee to heaven*

or to hell" ʻ(II.i.63-64). *Now he says* "Banquo, thy soul's flight,/If
it find heaven, must find it out to-night." *In both cases, Macbeth
sends his victims to heaven and himself to hell. Often the oblique
angle is more significant than the direct angle, just as, for example, Pat's description of Mike is more revealing about Pat than
about Mike. Certainly Macbeth's false description of Banquo is
a true description of himself, and the murderers' description of
themselves describes Macbeth's fate.*

*Again, the literal use of blood, time, and darkness in this scene
becomes a cluster of symbolic images signifying death, consequence, and evil. The* "dark hour" *of Banquo's death is one more
evil shoot from the prophetic* "seeds of time" *(I.iii.58) planted by
the evil witches back on the blasted heath.*

Scene II: The palace.

Enter LADY MACBETH *and a* Servant.

LADY MACBETH. Is Banquo gone from court?

SERVANT. Ay, madam, but returns again to-night.

LADY MACBETH. Say to the king, I would attend his leisure
 For a few words.

SERVANT.   Madam, I will. (*Exit*)

LADY MACBETH.   Nought's had, all's spent,
 Where our desire is got without content: 5
 'Tis safer to be that which we destroy
 Than by destruction dwell in doubtful joy.

(*Enter* MACBETH)

 How now, my lord! why do you keep alone,
 Of sorriest fancies your companions making,
 Using those thoughts which should indeed have died   10
 With them they think on? Things without all remedy
 Should be without regard: what's done is done.

Lady Macbeth's Remedy   *III.ii.1-12*

 *Lady Macbeth opens this domestic dialogue with some stone-
cold comfort.* "Things without all remedy/Should be without regard: what's done is done." *More disheartening than this spilt-
milk Stoicism is the irony of* "what's done is done." *What is done*

is final; it cannot be erased. The moment is irretrievable and ir-
revocable. Yet the moment is not final; its consequences last for-
ever. What happens in an instant of time lasts for a foreverness
of eternity. The murder of Duncan not only endures to damn
Macbeth but also to spawn more murders. Far from being a com-
fort, Lady Macbeth's words come closer to a curse. There is no
exit from the eternal moment. Such is the irony of finality.

MACBETH. We have scotch'd the snake, not kill'd it:
  She'll close and be herself, whilst our poor malice
  Remains in danger of her former tooth.   15
  But let the frame of things disjoint, both the worlds suffer,
  Ere we will eat our meal in fear and sleep
  In the affliction of these terrible dreams
  That shake us nightly: better be with the dead,
  Whom we, to gain our peace, have sent to peace,   20
  Than on the torture of the mind to lie
  In restless ecstasy. Duncan is in his grave;
  After life's fitful fever he sleeps well;
  Treason has done his worst: nor steel, nor poison,
  Malice domestic, foreign levy, nothing,   25
  Can touch him further.

Macbeth's Mental Torture   *III.ii.13-26*

  Earlier when Macbeth murdered Duncan, he said prophetically,
"Glamis hath murdered sleep. . . . Macbeth shall sleep no more"
(II.ii.42-43). Now that he has the crown, for himself but not for
his descendants, Macbeth is afflicted by "terrible dreams" and
"torture of the mind." The dead Duncan "sleeps well" but Mac-
beth alive must endure "life's fitful fever" and "lie/In restless
ecstasy." There is no peace and security for those who want to
be king; there is only frustration and anxiety. Confesses Macbeth
(line 36 below), "O, full of scorpions is my mind, dear wife!"
Rather than suffer "these terrible dreams," Macbeth would pre-
fer that chaos come and "both the worlds suffer" (heaven and
earth). Such wishful nihilism is completely ironic because both
worlds are suffering and "the frame of things" is disjointed.

Sometime ago (II.iv.) Macbeth murdered the sun when he mur-
dered Duncan. King Duncan is at peace not primarily because
he is dead but because he is guiltless.

LADY MACBETH.   Come on;
  Gentle my lord, sleek o'er your rugged looks;
  Be bright and jovial among your guests to-night.
MACBETH. So shall I, love; and so, I pray, be you:
  Let your remembrance apply to Banquo;   30
  Present him eminence, both with eye and tongue:
  Unsafe the while, that we
  Must lave our honours in these flattering streams,
  And make our faces vizards to our hearts,
  Disguising what they are.
LADY MACBETH.   You must leave this.   35
MACBETH. O, full of scorpions is my mind, dear wife!
  Thou know'st that Banquo, and his Fleance, lives.
LADY MACBETH. But in them nature's copy's not eterne.
MACBETH. There's comfort yet; they are assailable;
  Then be thou jocund: ere the bat hath flown   40
  His cloister'd flight, ere to black Hecate's summons
  The shard-borne beetle with his drowsy hums
  Hath rung night's yawning peal, there shall be done
  A deed of dreadful note.
LADY MACBETH.   What's to be done?
MACBETH. Be innocent of the knowledge, dearest chuck,   45
  Till thou applaud the deed. Come, seeling night,
  Scarf up the tender eye of pitiful day;
  And with thy bloody and invisible hand
  Cancel and tear to pieces that great bond
  Which keeps me pale! Light thickens; and the crow   50
  Makes wing to the rooky wood:
  Good things of day begin to droop and drowse;
  Whiles night's black agents to their preys do rouse.
  Thou marvell'st at my words: but hold thee still:
  Things bad begun make strong themselves by ill.   55
  So, prithee, go with me. (*Exeunt*)

As murder becomes a habit, Macbeth becomes more aggressive. Before the first murder of Duncan, Lady Macbeth told Macbeth to be the hypocrite and "look like the innocent flower,/But be the serpent under 't" (I.v.76-77). Now, before the second murder of Banquo, Macbeth tells Lady Macbeth to "make our faces vizards to our hearts,/Disguising what they are." In the first murder Lady Macbeth bids "thick night" to come (I.v.51); in the second, it is Macbeth who bids "seeling night" to come. (To seel is to sew up the eyelids of a hawk.) Earlier Macbeth trembled and obeyed his resolute wife. Now he resolutely takes the initiative without even informing his wife of his plot to murder Banquo and Fleance. As murder becomes cyclic, Macbeth becomes more resolved.

The dominant imagery in this richly poetic passage is light turning to darkness: the obscuring of good by evil and of clear reason by clouded passion. Macbeth not only murders the sleep of night, but also the light of day. Whatever is fair, Macbeth makes it foul, so that "innocent sleep" (II.ii.36) becomes "terrible dreams" (III.ii.18). Although the light and dark imagery expresses what Macbeth is doing to Scotland, it more deeply reveals what is happening to Macbeth himself. Symbolic of Macbeth's entire career is the image, "Light thickens." Beginning in a heaven of "Golden opinions" (I.vii.33), Macbeth becomes one of "night's black agents" and, as "Light thickens," falls to "murky" hell (V.i.40), ending as "black Macbeth" (IV.iii.52), the "fiend of Scotland" (IV.iii.233). The entire direction of the play is downward, light thickening from fair to foul. Like Lucifer, Macbeth is the bright creator of darkness, his own.

Scene III: A park near the palace.

Enter three Murderers.

FIRST MURDERER. But who did bid thee join with us?
THIRD MURDERER.   Macbeth.
SECOND MURDERER. He needs not our mistrust, since he delivers

Our offices and what we have to do
To the direction just.

FIRST MURDERER.   Then stand with us.
The west yet glimmers with some streaks of day.   5
Now spurs the lated traveller apace
To gain the timely inn; and near approaches
The subject of our watch.

THIRD MURDERER.   Hark! I hear horses.

BANQUO (*within*). Give us a light there, ho!

SECOND MURDERER.   Then 'tis he: the rest
That are within the note of expectation   10
Already are i' the court.

FIRST MURDERER.   His horses go about.

THIRD MURDERER. Almost a mile: but he does usually,
So all men do, from hence to the palace gate
Make it their walk.

SECOND MURDERER.   A light, a light!

(*Enter* BANQUO, *and* FLEANCE *with a torch*)

THIRD MURDERER.   'Tis he.

FIRST MURDERER. Stand to 't.

BANQUO. It will be rain to-night.

FIRST MURDERER.   Let it come down. (*They set*
upon BANQUO)

BANQUO. O, treachery! Fly, good Fleance, fly, fly, fly!
Thou mayst revenge. O slave! (*Dies.* FLEANCE *escapes*)

THIRD MURDERER. Who did strike out the light?

FIRST MURDERER.   Was't not the way?

THIRD MURDERER. There's but one down; the son is fled.

SECOND MURDERER.   We have
lost   20
Best half of our affair.

FIRST MURDERER. Well, let's away, and say how much is done.
(*Exeunt*)

The Murder of Banquo   *III.iii.*

It is always orthodox to ask where the third murderer came
from. Despite all unorthodox answers, the obvious answer is that

Macbeth sent the third murderer to insure the deaths of Banquo and Fleance by increasing the odds to three against two. Despite these odds, Fleance escapes. In fact, the ultimate odds are always against Macbeth. He earlier killed Duncan, but Malcolm and Donalbain escaped. He now kills Banquo but Fleance escapes. And he will later kill Lady Macduff and her children, but Macduff will escape. Macbeth has the imperial power to kill, but fortunately it is limited by a higher imperialism that saves Scotland's saviors.

The setting of the scene symbolizes the event. Although 'The west yet glimmers with some streaks of day," Banquo does not "gain the timely inn." For Banquo, the light of life is untimely put out by the murderous night. But for Fleance, who again carries a torch as he did earlier (at the beginning of II.i), the light of life survives dark death. Ironically, this survival depends on extinguishing the torch and flying in the night. (Where Fleance flies, we never learn.)

Scene IV:*The same. Hall in the palace.*

A *banquet prepared. Enter* MACBETH, LADY MACBETH, ROSS, LENNOX, Lords, *and* Attendants.

MACBETH. You know your own degrees; sit down: at first
And last the hearty welcome.

LORDS.   Thanks to your majesty.

MACBETH. Ourself will mingle with society,
And play the humble host.
Our hostess keeps her state, but in best time   5
We will require her welcome.

LADY MACBETH. Pronounce it for me, sir, to all our friends;
For my heart speaks they are welcome.

(First Murderer *appears at the door*)

MACBETH. See, they encounter thee with their hearts' thanks.
Both sides are even: here I'll sit i' the midst: 10
Be large in mirth; anon we'll drink a measure
The table round. (*Approaching the door*) There's blood
upon thy face.

MURDERER. 'Tis Banquo's then.

MACBETH. 'Tis better thee without than he within.
  Is he dispatch'd?   15

MURDERER. My lord, his throat is cut; that I did for him.

MACBETH. Thou art the best o' the cut-throats; yet he's good
  That did the like for Fleance: if thou didst it,
  Thou art the nonpareil.

MURDERER.   Most royal sir,
  Fleance is 'scaped.   20

MACBETH. Then comes my fit again: I had else been perfect,
  Whole as the marble, founded as the rock,
  As broad and general as the casing air:
  But now I am cabin'd, cribb'd, confined, bound in
  To saucy doubts and fears. But Banquo's safe?   25

MURDERER. Ay, my good lord: safe in a ditch he bides,
  With twenty trenched gashes on his head;
  The least a death to nature.

MACBETH.   Thanks for that.
  There the grown serpent lies; the worm that's fled
  Hath nature that in time will venom breed,   30
  No teeth for the present. Get thee gone: to-morrow
  We'll hear, ourselves, again. (*Exit Murderer*)

LADY MACBETH.   My royal lord,
  You do not give the cheer: the feast is sold
  That is not often vouch'd, while 'tis a-making,
  'Tis given with welcome: to feed were best at home;   35
  From thence the sauce to meat is ceremony;
  Meeting were bare without it.

MACBETH.   Sweet remembrancer!
  Now, good digestion wait on appetite,
  And health on both!

LENNOX.   May't please your highness sit.

The Banquet Begins   *III.iv.1-39*

  *At the banquet Macbeth says he will "play the humble host";
and indeed he does, just as he played it for Duncan. Though he*

*is still the hypocrite, he is now a more self-possessed hypocrite.
No longer does he care about choking on "Amen" or discoloring
the ocean (II.ii). He is becoming more and more conscience-
proof, but not completely, as the rest of the scene reveals. His
sense of values has become severely dislocated. For Macbeth
good is evil, and evil is good. Banquo's death is Macbeth's life
and freedom. And Fleance alive enslaves Macbeth and brings his
"fit again." To the evil, the good are evil. Hence Banquo and
Fleance are serpent and worm to the real serpent Macbeth. Foul
sees everything fair as foul, and everything foul as fair. Thus,
"in time" the fleeing Fleance (punningly named) "will venom
breed," that is, breed venom for Macbeth but medicine for Scotland. The double themes of foul-fair and time-consequence are
reflected in the abortive murder of father and son. If Macbeth's
health depends on his "good digestion" and "appetite," Macbeth
is deathly sick. Since the night Macbeth sent Duncan to heaven,
Macbeth's appetite has never been the same.*

(*The Ghost of* BANQUO *enters, and sits in* MACBETH's *place*)

MACBETH. Here had we now our country's honour roof'd,   40
   Were the graced person of our Banquo present;
   Who may I rather challenge for unkindness
   Than pity for mischance!
ROSS.   His absence, sir,
   Lays blame upon his promise. Please 't your highness
   To grace us with your royal company.   45
MACBETH. The table 's full.
LENNOX.   Here is a place reserved, sir.
MACBETH. Where?
LENNOX. Here, my good lord. What is 't that moves your highness?
MACBETH. Which of you have done this?
LORDS.   What, my good lord?
MACBETH. Thou canst not say I did it: never shake   50
   Thy gory locks at me.
ROSS. Gentlemen, rise; his highness is not well.
LADY MACBETH. Sit, worthy friends: my lord is often thus,
   And hath been from his youth: pray you, keep seat;

The fit is momentary; upon a thought   55
He will again be well: if much you note him,
You shall offend him and extend his passion:
Feed, and regard him not. Are you a man?

MACBETH. Ay, and a bold one, that dare look on that
Which might appal the devil.

LADY MACBETH.   O proper stuff!   60
This is the very painting of your fear:
This is the air-drawn dagger which, you said,
Led you to Duncan. O, these flaws and starts,
Impostors to true fear, would well become
A woman's story at a winter's fire,   65
Authorized by her grandam. Shame itself!
Why do you make such faces? When all's done,
You look but on a stool.

MACBETH. Prithee, see there! behold! look! lo! how say you?
Why, what care I? If thou canst nod, speak too.   70
If charnel-houses and our graves must send
Those that we bury back, our monuments
Shall be the maws of kites. (*Ghost vanishes*)

LADY MACBETH.   What, quite unmann'd in folly?

MACBETH. If I stand here, I saw him.

LADY MACBETH.   Fie, for shame!

MACBETH. Blood hath been shed ere now, i' the olden time,   75
Ere humane statute purged the gentle weal;
Ay, and since too, murders have been perform'd
Too terrible for the ear: the time has been,
That, when the brains were out, the man would die,
And there an end; but now they rise again,   80
With twenty mortal murders on their crowns,
And push us from our stools: this is more strange
Than such a murder is.

LADY MACBETH.   My worthy lord,
Your noble friends do lack you.

MACBETH.   I do forget.
Do not muse at me, my most worthy friends;   85
I have a strange infirmity, which is nothing

To those that know me. Come, love and health to all;
Then I'll sit down. Give me some wine; fill full.
I drink to the general joy o' the whole table,
And to our dear friend Banquo, whom we miss;　　　　90
Would he were here! to all, and him, we thirst,
And all to all.

LORDS.　　　　Our duties, and the pledge.

(*Re-enter* Ghost)

MACBETH. Avaunt! and quit my sight! let the earth hide thee!
Thy bones are marrowless, thy blood is cold;
Thou hast no speculation in those eyes　　　　95
Which thou dost glare with!

LADY MACBETH.　　　　Think of this, good peers,
But as a thing of custom: 'tis no other;
Only it spoils the pleasure of the time.

MACBETH. What man dare, I dare:
Approach thou like the rugged Russian bear,　　　　100
The arm'd rhinoceros, or the Hyrcan tiger;
Take any shape but that, and my firm nerves
Shall never tremble: or be alive again,
And dare me to the desert with thy sword;
If trembling I inhabit then, protest me　　　　105
The baby of a girl. Hence, horrible shadow!
Unreal mockery, hence! (*Ghost vanishes*)
　　　　　　　　Why, so: being gone,
I am a man again. Pray you, sit still.

LADY MACBETH. You have displaced the mirth, broke the good
　　meeting,
With most admired disorder.

MACBETH.　　　　Can such things be,　　　　110
And overcome us like a summer's cloud,
Without our special wonder? You make me strange
Even to the disposition that I owe,
When now I think you can behold such sights,
And keep the natural ruby of your cheeks,　　　　115
When mine is blanch'd with fear.

ROSS.　　　　What sights, my lord?

LADY MACBETH. I pray you, speak not; he grows worse and
   worse;
   Question enrages him. At once, good night:
   Stand not upon the order of your going,
   But go at once.
LENNOX.   Good night; and better health   120
   Attend his majesty!
LADY MACBETH.   A kind good night to all!
                (*Exeunt all but* MACBETH *and* LADY MACBETH)

Banquo Returns to the Banquet   *III.iv.40-121*

   *This great banquet scene with the ghost of Banquo was in-
vented by Shakespeare; it is not found in Holinshed's Chronicles,
Shakespeare's source. For those who are curious-minded about
Shakespeare's creative mind, here is an opportunity to observe
what Shakespeare adds and emphasizes on his own. Does he
complicate actions or reactions, increase suspense or irony, ex-
plore the exterior or the interior, enrich the colors or deepen the
perspective? In short, what added dimension of reality does
Shakespeare create with this original scene? He presents, in brief,
the interior vision of a tortured mind from the vanishing point
of unassailable anxiety. Shakespeare's problem here is to express
the state of Macbeth's spirit in visible, dramatic action. He therefore creates a surrealistic ghost and a ritualistic banquet.*
   *If surrealism finds a second reality floating in the subconscious
mind, uncontrolled by rational logic and incongruous with ordinary experience, then Macbeth's encounter with Banquo's ghost
may be said to be surrealistic. To Lady Macbeth, who is unaware
of Banquo's murder, the ghost is unreal. Macbeth, she scolds, is
ruining the dinner with a fit of false fear, an attack of spiritual
hypochondria. What Macbeth sees, she insists, is only a stool, not
a gory ghost. But to Macbeth, turbulent with anxiety, the surrealistic is more real than the realistic; the ghost is more real
than the stool. Its spectral realism belongs to a second reality of
shadows and mockery where foul cannot be masked with fair,
where hypocrisy collapses and invisible guilt becomes visible.*

The "gory locks," the "horrible shadow," and the "Unreal mockery" all show Macbeth how foul his foulness really is. Surrealism gives Macbeth a new knowledge of reality, not only its true ugliness but its utmost anxiety.

The utmost anxiety lies in the discovery that Macbeth can kill Banquo but not Banquo's ghost. "The time has been/That, when the brains were out, the man would die,/And there an end; but now they rise again . . . this is more strange/Than such a murder is." It is "more strange" realistically, but not surrealistically. Realistically, Macbeth says, "What man dare, I dare." Surrealistically, however, Macbeth goes beyond the limits of man, as he had said much earlier, "I dare do all that may become a man;/Who dares do more is none" (I.vii.46-47). Realistically, Macbeth would dare to fight a ferocious bear, rhinoceros, or tiger. Should Banquo take such a shape, Macbeth's "firm nerves" would never tremble. However, Banquo in the shape of a ghastly ghost appalls Macbeth, and he dare not fight. A tiger is an assailable, vulnerable object of human fear. A phantom is no object, unassailable and invulnerable: Hence it is a surrealistic anxiety, not a realistic fear. A tiger snarls in the jungle and can be killed; but Macbeth finds a ghost snarling within himself, an anxiety that cannot be killed. Anxiety is invulnerable because its source is death. Macbeth cannot kill Banquo again; he is already dead. Banquo alive is a fear; Banquo dead is an anxiety. Fear is realistic; anxiety is surrealistic. The ghost is surrealistically real, not really real. Macbeth suffers from the double anxiety of guilt and death. There is no escape from either. His very denial of guilt proclaims his guilt. "Thou canst not say I did it: never shake/Thy gory locks at me." Here the hallucination of the ghost comes after the murder; earlier with Duncan, the hallucination of "the air-drawn dagger" came before the murder. Because the dead do not stay dead, Macbeth is torn by the anxiety of death and guilt. Since there is no escape from this unassailable anxiety, the best Macbeth can do is to try to transform it into some assailable fear, like killing something that can be killed in the attempt to kill that which cannot be killed. Hence murder becomes a futile and wanton cure for something incurable, a cancerous therapy. Banquo has been removed from life as far as Macbeth's fear could remove him, but it was not far enough.

The banquet scene itself could be interpreted as a ritualistic parody, that is, a parodistic transformation of the sacrament of the Holy Eucharist. The Lord's supper becomes the banquet; the true presence of the sacrificed Christ, risen and glorified, becomes the risen ghost of bloody Banquo. With double irony, Macbeth makes a consecrating prayer "to our dear friend Banquo, whom we miss;/Would he were here!" Macbeth's prayers are answered. The spiritual body and blood of "the graced person of our Banquo [is] present," much to Macbeth's horror; if the physical Banquo were there instead, the horror would be dispelled. What makes the banquet scene an unholy parody of Holy Communion is that long ago, immediately after the murder of Duncan, Macbeth forsook his right to say "Amen" (II.ii.29). Macbeth is an exile from prayer and from grace. True communion conveys grace to the believer and strengthens and refreshes the soul in a reunion with God through Christ. Banquo's ghost reunites Macbeth with the inescapable anxiety of guilt and death. Hence the banquet scene is a ritualistic parody of the sacrament of the Holy Eucharist, a Last Supper in which nothing is eaten, a parodistic transformation of salvation into damnation. Parody must be used because Macbeth's values have become inauthentic.

Shakespeare invented this great banquet scene with its deaf-mute ghost to show that the consequences of assailable fear become unassailable anxiety. Because of the uninhabited grave of "our dear friend Banquo," Macbeth discovers, on an empty stomach, that he lives in an invulnerable world, a world in which the dead cannot be eliminated and guilt cannot be killed.

MACBETH. It will have blood; they say, blood will have blood:
　Stones have been known to move and trees to speak;
　Augurs and understood relations have
　By magot-pies and choughs and rooks brought forth　　125
　The secret'st man of blood. What is the night?
LADY MACBETH. Almost at odds with morning, which is which.

MACBETH. How say'st thou, that Macduff denies his person
  At our great bidding?
LADY MACBETH.   Did you send to him, sir?
MACBETH. I hear it by the way; but I will send: 130
  There's not a one of them but in his house
  I keep a servant fee'd. I will to-morrow,
  And betimes I will, to the weird sisters:
  More shall they speak; for now I am bent to know,
  By the worst means, the worst. For mine own good,   135
  All causes shall give way: I am in blood
  Stepp'd in so far that, should I wade no more,
  Returning were as tedious as go o'er:
  Strange things I have in head, that will to hand;
  Which must be acted ere they may be scann'd.   140
LADY MACBETH. You lack the season of all natures, sleep.
MACBETH. Come, we'll to sleep. My strange and self-abuse
  Is the initiate fear that wants hard use:
  We are yet but young in deed. (*Exeunt*)

Point of No Return   *III.iv.122-144*

*For Macbeth, bloody violence is becoming a way of life. So
far has he "Outrun the pauser, reason" (II.iii.117) that violence
of mind is a normal habit. When everybody is distrusted, everybody must be killed. Macduff is next. Violence for violence's sake,
blood for blood's sake, becomes the inevitable consequence of
universal fear. Yet Macbeth knows a Nemesis will come even to
"The secret'st man of blood." Looking backward to "even-handed
justice" (I.vii.10), Macbeth knows "blood will have blood." And
looking forward to moving Birnam wood (V.v), we realize how
"Stones have been known to move and trees to speak." At the
present moment, when the night, like Macbeth's life, is "Almost
at odds with morning," Macbeth is at the point of no return. He
is "in blood/Stepp'd in so far that . . . Returning were as tedious
as go o'er." Macbeth will soon be wading in blood up to his eye-
brows. Meanwhile, he can try to sleep, but he murdered "innocent sleep" (II.ii.30) long ago. It may be an invulnerable world,
but it is also a bloody red world.*

Scene V: A heath.

Thunder. Enter the three WITCHES, *meeting* HECATE.

FIRST WITCH. Why, how now, Hecate! you look angerly.
HECATE. Have I not reason, beldams as you are,
    Saucy and overbold? How did you dare
    To trade and traffic with Macbeth
    In riddles and affairs of death;   5
    And I, the mistress of your charms,
    The close contriver of all harms,
    Was never call'd to bear my part,
    Or show the glory of our art?
    And, which is worse, all you have done   10
    Hath been but for a wayward son,
    Spiteful and wrathful, who, as others do,
    Loves for his own ends, not for you.
    But make amends now: get you gone,
    And at the pit of Acheron   15
    Meet me i' the morning: thither he
    Will come to know his destiny:
    Your vessels and your spells provide,
    Your charms and every thing beside.
    I am for the air; this night I'll spend   20
    Unto a dismal and fatal end:
    Great business must be wrought ere noon:
    Upon the corner of the moon
    There hangs a vaporous drop profound;
    I'll catch it ere it come to ground: 25
    And that distill'd by magic sleights
    Shall raise such artificial sprites
    As by the strength of their illusion
    Shall draw him on to his confusion:
    He shall spurn fate, scorn death, and bear   30
    His hopes 'bove wisdom, grace and fear:
    And you all know, security
    Is mortals' chiefest enemy.
        (*Music and a song within:* "Come away, come away," &c.)
    Hark! I am call'd: my little spirit, see,
        Sits in a foggy cloud, and stays for me. (*Exit*)   35

FIRST WITCH. Come let's make haste; she'll soon
be back again. (*Exeunt*)

Hecate   III.v

*In this scene, generally recognized not to be by Shakespeare,
Macbeth's doom is foretold in iambic cadences. The classical allusions tell us that Macbeth is en route to hell, in case we were
in doubt. Not only is the Acheron a river in hell, but Hecate
herself is queen of the witches and of black magic. Her triple
roles are goddess of the underworld, goddess of the crossroads on
earth, and goddess of the moon. At the crossroads Macbeth has
taken the low road to the underworld. As moon goddess, Hecate
refers to "a vaporous drop" and "a foggy cloud," watery parallels
to "the fog and filthy air" of the three witches (I.i.11). In the
present pagan context, water symbolizes passion, and mist (clouds
and fog) symbolizes intellectual confusion, both symbolic of Macbeth's mental state. In such a state where reason gives way to
peremptory passion, Macbeth indeed bears "His hopes 'bove
wisdom, grace and fear." Hecate knows that "security/Is mortals'
chiefest enemy" because in desperately trying to achieve security,
Macbeth loses it. (Security in this passage is frequently taken to
mean confidence or overconfidence. I disagree; security meaning
certainty and freedom from doubt makes profounder sense.)
Security is something that neither Macbeth nor any man can gain;
hence its pursuit is always ironic. The only security is the will-
ingness to accept insecurity, and this Macbeth will not do. His
goddess is the false goddess Hecate.*

*Throughout the play, pagan references (Hecate, Gorgon, Tar-
quin, the witches) often express the dark evil of the murder;
whereas Christian references (Golgotha, the Lord's temple, saints
and angels) interpret the deed as an act of crucifixion (Duncan)
and damnation (Macbeth).*

Scene VI: Forres. The palace.

Enter LENNOX *and another* Lord.

LENNOX. My former speeches have but hit your thoughts,
Which can interpret further: only, I say,

Things have been strangely borne. The gracious Duncan
Was pitied of Macbeth: marry, he was dead:
And the right-valiant Banquo walk'd too late;   5
Whom, you may say, if 't please you, Fleance kill'd,
For Fleance fled: men must not walk too late.
Who cannot want the thought how monstrous
It was for Malcolm and for Donalbain
To kill their gracious father? damned fact!   10
How it did grieve Macbeth! did he not straight
In pious rage the two delinquents tear,
That were the slaves of drink and thralls of sleep?
Was not that nobly done? Ay, and wisely too;
For 'twould have anger'd any heart alive   15
To hear the men deny 't. So that, I say,
He has borne all things well: and I do think
That had he Duncan's sons under his key—
As, an 't please heaven, he shall not—they should find
What 'twere to kill a father; so should Fleance.   20
But, peace! for from broad words and 'cause he fail'd
His presence at the tyrant's feast, I hear
Macduff lives in disgrace: sir, can you tell
Where he bestows himself?

LORD.   The son of Duncan,
From whom this tyrant holds the due of birth,   25
Lives in the English court, and is received
Of the most pious Edward with such grace
That the malevolence of fortune nothing
Takes from his high respect: thither Macduff
Is gone to pray the holy king, upon his aid   30
To wake Northumberland and warlike Siward:
That, by the help of these—with Him above
To ratify the work—we may again
Give to our tables meat, sleep to our nights,
Free from our feasts and banquets bloody knives,   35
Do faithful homage and receive free honours:
All which we pine for now: and this report
Hath so exasperate the king that he
Prepares for some attempt of war.

LENNOX.   Sent he to Macduff?

LORD. He did: and with an absolute "Sir, not I,"   40
  The cloudy messenger turns me his back,
  And hums, as who should say "You'll rue the time
  That clogs me with this answer."

LENNOX.   And that well might
  Advise him to a caution, to hold what distance
  His wisdom can provide. Some holy angel   45
  Fly to the court of England and unfold
  His message ere he come, that a swift blessing
  May soon return to this our suffering country
  Under a hand accursed!

LORD.   I'll send my prayers with him.

                                    (*Exeunt*)

Macduff Seeks Help   *III.vi*

Lennox, with cautious irony, and the forthright Lord add up the score against "this tyrant" Macbeth. No one is fooled that the sons (Malcolm, Donalbain, and Fleance) have murdered their fathers (Duncan and Banquo). What appeared foul now appears fair, and what appeared fair (Macbeth), now appears foul. To relieve his "suffering country/Under a hand accursed," Macduff goes to England for help, both human and divine help. He needs soldiers and "Him above/To ratify the work." Since no "holy angel" beats Macduff "to the court of England," Macduff himself must be that "holy angel." The counter-Macbeth movement is underway.

ACT III SUMMARY

RECOIL AND RELOAD

Macbeth's gains and losses begin to emerge. He has gained the bejeweled crown from "the gracious Duncan" (III.i.66), but he has lost "mine eternal jewel" or soul "to the common enemy of man," the devil (III.i.68-69). He has gained the power of the world but lost all integrity and moral authority. Macbeth cannot escape living in two worlds, the moral world of right and the material world of might. He made the gamble (I.vii.7) that he could trade the former world for the latter. He now discovers it may have been a bad bet. He has been cheated. He gives his "eternal jewell" but in return gets only "a fruitless crown" (III.i.61). The material world holds out on him. He gets Banquo, but not Fleance. Apparently Macbeth is playing the power game against a stacked deck of cards. He thought he was promised a royal flush. "All hail, Macbeth, that shalt be king hereafter!" promised the witches (I.iii.50). Macbeth won the king all right, but the ace was dealt to Banquo: "Thou shalt get kings, though thou be none" (I.iii.67). Thus, says Macbeth, "For Banquo's issue have I filed [defiled] my mind" (III.i.65). Gambling with witches is slippery business, especially if there is no chance to shuffle the cards.

Actually the cards have been fairly shuffled by "even-handed justice" (I.vii.10). It is Macbeth who is trying to stack the deck. His own failure drives him deeper into blood. It is through failure that he discovers "the torture of the mind" (III.ii.21) in the certainty of insecurity. The desperate disenchantment with enchantment creates the surrealism of Banquo's "gory locks" shaking guilt and anxiety all over the banquet table. If the living are a threat to Macbeth's "fruitless crown," the dead are a menace to his "eternal jewel." Both body and soul are endangered by mortal and immortal insecurity. Ironically, if Macbeth trades the moral world for the material world, he finds no refuge in either. The material world escapes in Fleance, and the moral world returns in Banquo's ghost. Macbeth cannot win for losing in both worlds. Hence he lives a bloated outcast in the material world and a shriveled castout in the moral world.

Despite the unequivocal fact that time is working against Macbeth, bringing restless anxiety, the hardened Macbeth becomes stronger in evil, while Lady Macbeth becomes weaker. No longer does he need the heady prompting of Lady Macbeth to wade deeper into blood. The noble warrior has become the ruthless tyrant. When Macbeth murdered Duncan, he created chaos in nature and darkened the sun, strangling "the travelling lamp" so that "darkness does the face of earth entomb" (II.iv.7-9). When Macbeth murders Banquo, "Light thickens" (III.ii.50) into cloudy night (III.iii.16). In both cases Macbeth denigrates himself. In destroying his world, he destroys himself. Violating the social structure of the land, Macbeth destroys his world, first by killing his king and then, king himself, by killing his subjects. The consequence of such malicious homicide is a stinging, poisonous mind "full of scorpions" (III.ii.36). It is also a disinherited mind, one that tried to trade "the life to come" for "this bank and shoal of time" (I.vii.6-7) and lost both.

ACT IV

Scene I: *A cavern. In the middle, a boiling cauldron.*

Thunder. Enter the three Witches.

FIRST WITCH. Thrice the brinded cat hath mew'd.
SECOND WITCH. Thrice and once the hedge-pig whined.
THIRD WITCH. Harpier cries 'Tis time, 'tis time.
FIRST WITCH. Round about the cauldron go;
  In the poison'd entrails throw.   5
  Toad, that under cold stone
  Days and nights has thirty one
  Swelter'd venom sleeping got,
  Boil thou first i' the charmed pot.
ALL. Double, double toil and trouble;   10
  Fire burn, and cauldron bubble.
SECOND WITCH. Fillet of a fenny snake,
  In the cauldron boil and bake;
  Eye of newt and toe of frog,
  Wool of bat and tongue of dog,   15
  Adder's fork and blind-worm's sting,
  Lizard's leg and howlet's wing,
  For a charm of powerful trouble,
  Like a hell-broth boil and bubble.
ALL. Double, double toil and trouble;   20
  Fire burn and cauldron bubble.
THIRD WITCH. Scale of dragon, tooth of wolf,
  Witches' mummy, maw and gulf

Of the ravin'd salt-sea shark,
Root of hemlock digg'd i' the dark,   25
Liver of blaspheming Jew,
Gall of goat, and slips of yew
Sliver'd in the moon's eclipse,
Nose of Turk and Tartar's lips,
Finger of birth-strangled babe   30
Ditch-deliver'd by a drab,
Make the gruel thick and slab:
Add thereto a tiger's chaudron,
For the ingredients of our cauldron.
ALL. Double, double toil and trouble;   35
Fire burn and cauldron bubble.
SECOND WITCH. Cool it with a baboon's blood,
Then the charm is firm and good.
(*Enter* HECATE *to the other three* Witches)
HECATE. O, well done! I commend your pains;
And every one shall share i' the gains: 40
And now about the cauldron sing,
Likes elves and fairies in a ring,
Enchanting all that you put in.
          (*Music and a song:* "Black spirits," &c. HECATE *retires*)
SECOND WITCH. By the pricking of my thumbs,
Something wicked this way comes.   45
                    Open, locks,
                    Whoever knocks!

The Witches' Cauldron   *IV.i.1-47*

*When the witches first met Macbeth back on the heath, they
said, "Peace! the charm's wound up" (I.iii.37). In the present scene
we learn the wicked recipe for charming Macbeth, a "charmed
pot" full of "poison'd entrails" and "powerful trouble." The chief
ingredients for this "charm of powerful trouble" are malignant morsels of subhuman creatures—beasts, birds, and fish—and
pieces of unchristened human beings. This indigestible "hell-
broth" boils over with bestial poison. Hence whoever drinks it*

becomes charmed into a bloody beast, a subhuman monster. Macduff later refers to Macbeth as one of "our rarer monsters" (V.viii.25). By daring to do more than "may become a man" (I.vii.46), Macbeth descends the chain of being and becomes a beast. The net effect of this poisoned, bloody, bestial "hell-broth" is, therefore, to make Macbeth himself become a bloody beast.

A well-dressed man, aware of complementary colors, might match his socks and tie, even though his neck and ankles are widely separated. Shakespeare applies this aesthetic principle of repeated colors to repeated themes or motifs. Such thematic recurrence often forms a revealing pattern. Two such patterns, independent of the natural time-sequence of events, emerge in the present scene. First, the theme of the poisoned drink: It it prepared in the witches' cauldron; served by that "fourth witch," Lady Macbeth ("Go bid thy mistress [Lady Macbeth], when my drink is ready,/She strike upon the bell." II.i.31-32); drunk by Macbeth as the bell strikes, just before the murder of Duncan; and finally it was foretold and approved by "this even-handed justice [which] Commends the ingredients of our poison'd chalice/ To our own lips" (I.vii.10-120). Now we know that the "poison'd chalice" contained a "hell-broth." Although demonic witches stir the "charmed pot," it is divinely employed by "even-handed justice." A chalice, the goblet used at the Lord's Supper, contains the poison; the divine embraces the demonic in the image of the "poison'd chalice."

Second, the trochaic refrain of "Double, double toil and trouble": The "double" motif suggests the general theme of appearance and reality, foulness and fairness, equivocation and hypocrisy. Specifically, the double motif occurs earlier in Macbeth's double deception of Duncan. "He's here in double trust;/First, as I am his kinsman and his subject . . . then, as his host . . ." (I.vii.12-14). Later, the double motif occurs in the witches' deception of Macbeth. "And be these juggling fiends no more believed,/That palter with us in a double sense;/That keep the word of promise to our ear,/And break it to our hope" (V.viii.19-22). The motif "double toil and trouble" describes Macbeth deceived and Macbeth deceiving. Macbeth's double losses are the loss of clear reason expressed through the imagery of darkness and magic, and the loss of humanity expressed through the imagery of blood and beasts. Instead of returning to the witches in this scene, Macbeth should be on his knees, fasting.

(*Enter* MACBETH)

MACBETH. How now, you secret, black, and midnight hags!
  What is 't you do?
ALL.   A deed without a name.
MACBETH. I conjure you, by that which you profess,   50
  Howe'er you come to know it, answer me:
  Though you untie the winds and let them fight
  Against the churches; though the yesty waves
  Confound and swallow navigation up;
  Though bladed corn be lodged and trees blown down;   55
  Though castles topple on their warders' heads;
  Though palaces and pyramids do slope
  Their heads to their foundations; though the treasure
  Of nature's germens tumble all together,
  Even till destruction sicken; answer me   60
  To what I ask you.
FIRST WITCH.   Speak.
SECOND WITCH.   Demand.
THIRD WITCH.   We'll answer.
FIRST WITCH. Say, if thou 'dst rather hear it from our mouths,
  Or from our masters?
MACBETH.   Call 'em; let me see 'em.
FIRST WITCH. Pour in sow's blood, that hath eaten
  Her nine farrow; grease that's sweaten   65
  From the murderer's gibbet throw
  Into the flame.
ALL.   Come, high or low;
  Thyself and office deftly show!
(*Thunder. First* Apparition: *an armed Head*)
MACBETH. Tell me, thou unknown power,—
FIRST WITCH.   He knows thy thought:
  Hear his speech, but say thou nought.   70

FIRST APPARITION. Macbeth! Macbeth! Macbeth!
    beware Macduff;
  Beware the thane of Fife. Dismiss me. Enough. (*Descends*)
MACBETH. Whate'er thou art, for thy good caution, thanks;
  Thous hast harp'd my fear aright: but one word more,—
FIRST WITCH. He will not be commanded: here's another,   75
  More potent than the first.
(*Thunder. Second* Apparition: *a bloody Child*)
SECOND APPARITION. Macbeth! Macbeth! Macbeth!
MACBETH. Had I three ears, I 'ld hear thee.
SECOND APPARITION. Be bloody, bold, and resolute;
    laugh to scorn
  The power of man, for none of woman born   80
  Shall harm Macbeth. (*Descends*)
MACBETH. Then live, Macduff: what need I fear of thee?
  But yet I'll make assurance double sure,
  And take a bond of fate: thou shalt not live;
  That I may tell pale-hearted fear it lies,   85
  And sleep in spite of thunder.
(*Thunder. Third* Apparition: *a Child crowned,*
    with a tree in his hand)
                        What is this
  That rises like the issue of a king,
  And wears upon his baby-brow the round
  And top of sovereignty?
ALL.   Listen, but speak not to 't.
THIRD APPARITION. Be lion-mettled, proud; and take no care   90
  Who chafes, who frets, or where conspirers are:
  Macbeth shall never vanquish'd be until
  Great Birnam wood to high Dunsinane hill
  Shall come against him. (*Descends*)
MACBETH.   That will never be:
  Who can impress the forest, bid the tree   95
  Unfix his earth-bound root? Sweet bodements! good!
  Rebellion's head, rise never till the wood
  Of Birnam rise, and our high-placed Macbeth
  Shall live the lease of nature, pay his breadth
  To time and mortal custom.

Macbeth Meets the Three Apparitions   IV.i.48-100

There is no progress in hell, only desperate repetition. Macbeth's return to the "secret, black, and midnight hags" brings him right back to where he began. In his anxiety and insecurity, he now seeks reaffirmation, hoping to find and afraid to find. What he finds is denial wearing the mask of affirmation. The return to the witches leads to more peril-proof illusions.

Macbeth's first question—"What is 't you do?"—is unanswered because the answer—"A deed without a name"—is boiling, baking, and cooling, "a charm of powerful trouble" (IV.i.18) for the damnation of Macbeth. He commands that his questions be answered, even if it means universal destruction, letting "the treasurer/Of nature's germens [seeds] tumble all together,/Even till destruction sicken." The logical end of Macbeth's pursuit of security is biocide, the death of nature itself. Ironically, Macbeth would destroy all life to preserve his life.

The answers to Macbeth's future safety come in the form of three apparitions; an armed head (perhaps Macduff in the form of "Rebellion's head"); a bloody child (again Macduff, who was "from his mother's womb/Untimely ripp'd," V.viii.15-16); and a crowned child carrying a tree (Malcolm, who becomes king and orders the soldiers to cut boughs from Birnam wood to camouflage their advance to Dunsinane, V.iv). The armed head, the bloody child, and the crowned child represent the counter-Macbeth movement: rebellion against tyranny, sacrifice of the innocent (especially Macduff's family, IV.ii), and the rebirth of justice. For these particular apparitions to answer Macbeth's questions is in itself ironic. As Macbeth's deadly enemies, the apparitions are the last ones Macbeth should go to for advice. Moreover, their assuring answers are actually deadly temptations.

The first apparition warns Macbeth to "beware Macduff." This honest warning soon becomes a temptation to kill Macduff and his family. The second apparition tells Macbeth to "laugh to scorn/ The power of man, for none of woman born/Shall harm Macbeth." The temptation here is safety from "the power of man," especially Macduff. Clearly, the second apparition contradicts the first, although Macbeth does not know that Macduff was not "of woman born" but "from his mother's womb/Untimely ripp'd" (V.viii.15-16). *(Macduff's Caesarian birth makes him technically "none of woman born.") Yet the last laugh is on Macbeth; for if the "power of man" is really powerless, Macbeth, a man, must be powerless too. Hence he must "laugh to scorn" himself. A power beyond mortal power is working against the mortal Macbeth. The full irony of the first apparition's warning now emerges. Although Macbeth feels safe from Macduff, he decides to kill him just to "makes assurance double sure,/And take a bond of fate." It is the very butchery of killing Macduff's family that resolves Macduff to kill Macbeth in revenge. Macbeth seals his own fate in taking "a bond of fate." The third apparition tempts Macbeth into deeper pseudo-safety. "Macbeth shall never vanquish'd be until/Great Birnam wood to high Dunsinane hill/Shall come against him." The technicality of cutting and carrying boughs of Birnam wood to Dunsinane (V.iv) gives the lie to this impossible possibility. All the "Sweet bodements" are actually bitter bodements for Macbeth.*

Just as the three witches have led Macbeth into thinking fair is foul (I.iii), so the three apparitions similarly deceive him with half-truths. They say Macbeth is vulnerable to no man born of woman, but they do not say that "Macduff was from his mother's womb/Untimely ripp'd" (V.viii.15-16). They say Macbeth is safe until Birnam wood moves to Dunsinane, but they do not say that "every soldier [will] hew him down a bough/And bear 't before him" (V.iv.4-5). The apparitions, like the witches, know more than they reveal. Thus they immensely deceive "lion-mettled" Macbeth into thinking that he has more than mortal power, that he is safely autonomous.

Yet my heart   100
  Throbs to know one thing: tell me, if your art
  Can tell so much: shall Banquo's issue ever
  Reign in this kingdom?
ALL.   Seek to know no more.
MACBETH. I will be satisfied: deny me this,
  And an eternal curse fall on you! Let me know.   105
  Why sinks that cauldron? and what noise is this? (*Hautboys*)
FIRST WITCH. Show!

SECOND WITCH. Show!

THIRD WITCH. Show!

ALL. Show his eyes, and grieve his heart;   110

    Come like shadows, so depart!

(*A show of Eight* Kings, *the last with a glass in his hand;*

    BANQUO's *Ghost following*)

MACBETH. Thou art too like the spirit of Banquo; down!

    Thy crown does sear mine eye-balls. And thy hair,

    Thou other gold-bound brow, is like the first.

    A third is like the former. Filthy hags!   115

    Why do you show me this? A fourth! Start, eyes!

    What, will the line stretch out to the crack of doom?

    Another yet! A seventh! I'll see no more:

    And yet the eighth appears, who bears a glass

    Which show me many more; and some I see   120

    That two-fold balls and treble sceptres carry:

    Horrible sight! Now, I see, 'tis true;

    For the blood-bolter'd Banquo smiles upon me,

    And points at them for his. (*Apparitions vanish*)

      What, is this so?

FIRST WITCH. Ay, sir, all this is so: but why   125

    Stands Macbeth thus amazedly?

    Come, sisters, cheer we up his sprites,

    And show the best of our delights:

    I'll charm the air to give a sound,

    While you perform your antic round;   130

    That this great king may kindly say,

    Our duties did his welcome pay.

    (*Music. The Witches dance, and then vanish, with* HECATE)

MACBETH. Where are they? Gone? Let this pernicious hour

    Stand aye accursed in the calendar!

    Come in, without there!

(*Enter* LENNOX)

LENNOX.   What's your grace's will?   135

MACBETH. Saw you the weird sisters?

LENNOX   No, my lord.

MACBETH. Came they not by you?

LENNOX   No, indeed, my lord.

MACBETH. Infected be the air whereon they ride;
And damn'd all those that trust them! I did hear
The galloping of horse: who was't came by?   140
LENNOX. 'Tis two or three, my lord, that bring you word
Macduff is fled to England.
MACBETH.   Fled to England!
LENNOX. Ay, my good lord.
MACBETH. Time, thou anticipatest my dread exploits:
The flighty purpose never is o'ertook   145
Unless the deed go with it: from this moment
The very firstlings of my heart shall be
The firstlings of my hand. And even now,
To crown my thoughts with acts, be it thought and done:
The castle of Macduff I will surprise;   150
Seize upon Fife; give to the edge o' the sword
His wife, his babes, and all unfortunate souls
That trace him in his line. No boasting like a fool:
This deed I'll do before this purpose cool.
But no more sights!—Where are these gentlemen?   155
Come, bring me where they are. (*Exeunt*)

Macbeth Sees Eight Kings and One Ghost   *IV.i.100-156*

*Like the drunkard in the Porter scene (II.iii.30-40), Macbeth is
provoked and unprovoked. If the assurances of the three apparitions give Macbeth the feeling of security, the "show of Eight
Kings" and the vision of smiling "blood bolter'd Banquo" take it
all away again. The dissembling witches continue their game of
equivocation with Macbeth. They promise a prize that can give
Macbeth all power, but which consumes and leads to damnation.
Banquo's life is cut short, but his line will "stretch out to the
crack of doom." Macbeth will lose; Banquo will win. Macbeth is
outrageously enraged. He places an "eternal curse" on the
witches, ironically prophesying his own fate. He would "Let this
pernicious hour/Stand aye accursed in the calendar!" ironically
cursing the date in the calendar which he himself arranged. And
finally he says, "And damn'd [be] all those that trust them,"
ironically damning himself for trusting the witches. All future*

*promises have ended in accursed consequences, without rest or
peace. After the witches "Show his eyes, and grieve his heart,"
they vanish. "Where are they?" asks Macbeth. We might better
ask, where is Macbeth?*

*Blood-thirsty with despair, Macbeth again lets his violent pas-
sion "Outrun the pauser, reason" (II.iii.117). He learns of Macduff's defection and in retaliation plans an immediate massacre of
"The castle of Macduff." Any living Scotsman would think Macbeth now murders for the pleasure or the fashion of it. Murder
is no longer a ladder for ambition; it is a dissipation to relieve
desperation. The witches may be only greasy cooks, barely able
to stir the pot, but their "hell-broth" (IV.i.19) is appetizing enough
to transform the gluttonous Macbeth into a bloody beast. The
"charm of powerful trouble" (IV.i.18) was indeed "firm and good"
(IV.i.38). It worked.*

Scene II: Fife. MACDUFF's *castle.*

Enter LADY MACDUFF, *her* Son, *and* ROSS.

LADY MACDUFF. What had he done, to make him fly the land?
ROSS. You must have patience, madam.
LADY MACDUFF.   He had none:
   His flight was madness: when our actions do not,
   Our fears do make us traitors.
ROSS.   You know not
   Whether it was his wisdom or his fear.   5
LADY MACDUFF. Wisdom! to leave his wife, to leave his babes,
   His mansion and his titles in a place
   From whence himself does fly? He loves us not;
   He wants the natural touch: for the poor wren,
   The most diminutive of birds, will fight,   10
   Her young ones in her nest, against the owl.
   All is the fear and nothing is the love;
   As little is the wisdom, where the flight
   So runs against all reason.
ROSS.   My dearest coz,
   I pray you, school yourself: but for your husband,   15

He is noble, wise, judicious, and best knows
The fits o' the season. I dare not speak much further;
But cruel are the times, when we are traitors
And do not know ourselves, when we hold rumour
From what we fear, yet know not what we fear,   20
But float upon a wild and violent sea
Each way and move. I take my leave of you:
Shall not be long but I'll be here again:
Things at the worst will cease, or else climb upward
To what they were before. My pretty cousin,   25
Blessing upon you!

LADY MACDUFF. Father'd he is, and yet he's fatherless.

ROSS. I am so much a fool, should I stay longer,
It would be my disgrace and your discomfort:
I take my leave at once. (*Exit*)

LADY MACDUFF.   Sirrah, your father's dead: 30
And what will you do now? How will you live?

SON. As birds do, mother.

LADY MACDUFF.   What, with worms and flies?

SON. With what I get, I mean; and so do they.

LADY MACDUFF. Poor bird! thou 'ldst never fear the net nor lime,
The pitfall nor the gin.   35

SON. Why should I, mother? Poor birds they are not set for.
My father is not dead, for all your saying.

LADY MACDUFF. Yes, he is dead: how wilt thou do for a father?

SON. Nay, how will you do for a husband?

LADY MACDUFF. Why, I can buy me twenty at any market.   40

SON. Then you'll buy 'em to sell again.

LADY MACDUFF. Thou speak'st with all thy wit; and yet, i' faith,
With wit enough for thee.

SON. Was my father a traitor, mother?

LADY MACDUFF. Ay, that he was.   45

SON. What is a traitor?

LADY MACDUFF. Why, one that swears and lies.

SON. And be all traitors that do so?

LADY MACDUFF. Every one that does so is a traitor,
and must be hanged.   50

SON. And must they all be hanged that swear and lie?

LADY MACDUFF. Every one.

SON. Who must hang them?

LADY MACDUFF. Why, the honest men.

SON. Then the liars and swearers are fools, for there are liars and
swearers enow to beat the honest men and hang up them.

LADY MACDUFF. Now, God help thee, poor monkey! But how wilt
thou do for a father?   60

SON. If he were dead, you 'ld weep for him: if you would not, it
were a good sign that I should quickly have a new father.

LADY MACDUFF. Poor prattler, how thou talk'st!

(*Enter a* Messenger)

MESSENGER. Bless you, fair dame! I am not to you known,   65
Though in your state of honour I am perfect.
I doubt some danger does approach you nearly:
If you will take a homely man's advice,
Be not found here; hence, with your little ones.
To fright you thus, methinks, I am too savage;   70
To do worse to you were fell cruelty,
Which is too nigh your person. Heaven preserve you!
I dare abide no longer. (*Exit*)

LADY MACDUFF.   Whither should I fly?
I have done no harm. But I remember now
I am in this earthly world; where to do harm   75
Is often laudable, to do good sometime
Accounted dangerous folly: why then, alas,
Do I put up that womanly defence,
To say I have done no harm?

(*Enter* Murderers)   What are these faces?

FIRST MURDERER. Where is your husband?   80

LADY MACDUFF. I hope, in no place so unsanctified
Where such as thou mayst find him.

FIRST MURDERER.   He 's a traitor.

SON. Thou liest, thou shag-hair'd villain!

FIRST MURDERER.   What, you egg!
    (*Stabbing him*)
Young fry of treachery!

SON.   He has kill'd me, mother:
Run away, I pray you!   85
                (*Dies. Exit* LADY MACDUFF, *crying* "*Murder!*" *Exeunt
                Murders, following her*)

Macduff's Family Murdered   IV.ii

*As a link in the chain of dramatic action, this scene has a
double function: to blacken Macbeth's character as a wanton
butcher and to motivate Macduff's revenge for his slaughtered
family. Shakespeare had already driven both of these nails in—
Macbeth's character and Macduff's motivation—but here he
clinches them.*

*As a critique of Macduff by Lady Macduff, this scene ironi-
cally reveals a double standard of behavior in a world of justice
and injustice. Lady Macduff assumes that in a world in which
right is might, love and reason are natural. Conversely, in a world
in which might is right, these natural dispositions become unnatural fear and folly, so that innocence becomes guilt. The
natural condition of life and behavior is justice, order, peace.
The unnatural conditon is injustice, anarchy, and violence. Both
conditions are ironically illuminated by Lady Macduff's criticism
of Macduff as contrasted to her own actions. She begins by ask-
ing, "What had he done, to make him fly the land?" Later, however, when warned of the approach of Macbeth's faceless murderers, she says, "Whither should I fly?/I have done no harm."
Neither had Macduff. Now the shoe is on the other foot. If Macduff's "flight was madness," so be hers; only now she realizes
that "to do good [is] sometime/Accounted dangerous folly" and
that mere innocence is a "womanly defence." Again, Lady Macduff says her husband does not love his family. "He wants [lacks]
the natural touch"; (indeed he was "from his mother's womb/
Untimely ripp'd" (V.viii.15-16). In nature, even a tiny wren will
fight an owl to protect "Her young ones in her nest." Although
she idealizes the natural instinct of the wren, she warns her own
"Poor bird" to "fear the net." Protective love may be natural, but*

natural innocence must still fear the dangers of the world, again, just as Macduff feared them. One cannot live in the world by natural innocence alone. More contradictory is the "poor wren" and poor Lady Macduff herself. The wren loves her young and fights to protect them. Yet when the murderers come, the child is stabbed and Lady Macduff runs. If Macduff did not protect his wife, his wife does not protect her son. Cruelty and violence can change love into fear and make wisdom run "against all reason." Once again, when the first murderer asks where Macduff is, Lady Macduff replies, "I hope, in no place so unsanctified/Where such as thou mayst find him." Ironically, Macduff, in England, is in an sanctified country, but Lady Macduff, in Fife, is in an unsanctified country.

These various ironies do not obviate Macduff's culpability. Macduff, who underestimated Macbeth's savage cruelty, later acknowledges his own guilt as "Sinful Macduff" (IV.iii.224). Rather, these ironies reveal that no love is invulnerable to fear and that the unnatural condition becomes a naturalistic condition (i.e., brute survival) in an unnatural world where the king's subjects become objects and a "father'd" son becomes "fatherless." In a corrupted world where the villains outnumber the honest men, moral utilitarianism would seem to rule; that is, the immorality of the majority is moral. Or as Lady Macduff's precocious boy argues, the "honest men" cannot hang the traitors because there are enough "liars and swearers . . . to beat the honest men and hang up them." Fortunately, what is general practice is not always normative. Might may rule, but it cannot make itself thereby morally right. The entire play demonstrates this granite fact.

Macduff, of course, is a traitor to Macbeth, because Macbeth is a traitor to Scotland. Hence in being a traitor to a traitor, Macduff is loyal to Scotland. The rub is that Macduff must at the same time be disloyal to his family. It is a loyalty dilemma between family and country, and there is no painless solution, only the tragic sacrifice of an innocent mother and her child. This scene is a woman's scene, dominated by a woman's passionate, personal, ironic reasoning and by a woman's suffering and sacrifice for her husband.

Scene III: ENGLAND. *Before the* KING's *palace.*

Enter MALCOM *and* MACDUFF.

MALCOLM. Let us seek out some desolate shade, and there
    Weep our sad bosoms empty.

MACDUFF.   Let us rather
    Hold fast the mortal sword, and like good men
    Bestride our down-fall'n birthdom: each new morn
    New widows howl, new orphans cry, new sorrows   5
    Strike heaven on the face, that it resounds
    As if it felt with Scotland and yell'd out
    Like syllable of dolor.

MALCOLM.   What I believe, I'll wail;
    What know, believe; and what I can redress,
    As I shall find the time to friend, I will.   10
    What you have spoke, it may be so perchance.
    This tyrant, whose sole name blisters our tongues,
    Was once thought honest: you have loved him well;
    He hath not touch'd you yet. I am young; but something
    You may deserve of him through me, and wisdom   15
    To offer up a weak poor innocent lamb
    To appease an angry god.

MACDUFF. I am not treacherous.

MALCOLM.   But Macbeth is.
    A good and virtuous nature may recoil
    In an imperial charge. But I shall crave your pardon;   20
    That which you are my thoughts cannot transpose:
    Angels are bright still, though the brightest fell:
    Though all things foul would wear the brows of grace,
    Yet grace must still look so.

MACDUFF.   I have lost my hopes.

MALCOLM. Perchance even there where I did find my doubts. 25
    Why in that rawness left you wife and child,
    Those precious motives, those strong knots of love,
    Without leave-taking? I pray you,
    Let not my jealousies be your dishonours,
    But mine own safeties. You may be rightly just,   30
    Whatever I shall think.

MACDUFF.   Bleed, bleed, poor country!
  Great tyranny! lay thou thy basis sure,
  For goodness dare not check thee: wear thou thy wrongs;
  The title is affeer'd! Fare thee well, lord:
  I would not be the villain that thou think'st   35
  For the whole space that 's in the tyrant's grasp,
  And the rich East to boot.
MALCOLM.   Be not offended:
  I speak not as in absolute fear of you.
  I think our country sinks beneath the yoke;
  It weeps, it bleeds; and each new day a gash   40
  Is added to her wounds: I think withal
  There would be hands uplifted in my right;
  And here from gracious England have I offer
  Of goodly thousands: but, for all this,
  When I shall tread upon the tryant's head,   45
  Or wear it on my sword, yet my poor country
  Shall have more vices than it had before,
  More suffer and more sundry ways than ever,
  By him that shall succeed.
MACDUFF.   What should he be?
MALCOLM. It is myself I mean: in whom I know   50
  All the particulars of vice so grafted
  That, when they shall be open'd black Macbeth
  Will seem as pure as snow, and the poor state
  Esteem him as a lamb, being compared
  With my confineless harms.
MACDUFF.   Not in the legions   55
  Or horrid hell can come a devil more damn'd
  In evils to top Macbeth.
MALCOLM.   I grant him bloody,
  Luxurious, avaricious, false, deceitful,
  Sudden, malicious, smacking of every sin
  That has a name: but there's no bottom, none,   60
  In my voluptuousness: your wives, your daughters,
  Your matrons and your maids, could not fill up
  The cistern of my lust, and my desire

All continent impediments would o'erbear
That did oppose my will: better Macbeth   65
Than such an one to reign.

MACDUFF.   Boundless intemperance
In nature is a tyranny; it hath been
The untimely emptying of the happy throne
And fall of many kings. But fear not yet
To take upon you what is yours: you may   70
Convey your pleasures in a spacious plenty,
And yet seem cold, the time you may so hoodwink.
We have willing dames enough; there cannot be
That vulture in you, to devour so many
As will to greatness dedicate themselves,   75
Finding it so inclined.

MALCOLM.   With this there grows
In my most ill-composed affection such
A stanchless avarice that, were I king,
I should cut off the nobles for their lands,
Desire his jewels and this other's house: 80
And my more-having would be as a sauce
To make me hunger more; that I should forge
Quarrels unjust against the good and loyal,
Destroying them for wealth.

MACDUFF.   This avarice
Sticks deeper, grows with more pernicious root   85
Than summer-seeming lust, and it hath been
The sword of our slain kings: yet do not fear;
Scotland hath foisons to fill up your will,
Of your mere own: all these are portable,
With other graces weigh'd.   90

MALCOLM. But I have none: the king-becoming graces,
As justice, verity, temperance, stableness,
Bounty, perseverance, mercy, lowliness,
Devotion, patience, courage, fortitude,
I have no relish of them, but abound   95
In the division of each several crime,
Acting it many ways. Nay, had I power, I should
Pour the sweet milk of concord into hell,

Uproar the universal peace, confound
All unity on earth.

MACDUFF.   O Scotland, Scotland!   100

MALCOLM. If such a one be fit to govern, speak:
I am as I have spoken.

MACDUFF.   Fit to govern!
No, not to live. O nation miserable,
With an untitled tyrant bloody-scepter'd,
When shalt thou see thy wholesome days again,   105
Since that the truest issue of thy throne
By his own interdiction stands accursed,
And does blaspheme his breed? Thy royal father
Was a most sainted king: the queen that bore thee,
Oftener upon her knees than on her feet,   110
Died every day she lived. Fare thee well!
These evils thou repeat'st upon thyself
Have banish'd me from Scotland. O my breast,
Thy hope end here!

MALCOM.   Macduff, this noble passion,
Child of integrity, hath from my soul   115
Wiped the black scruples, reconciled my thoughts
To thy good truth and honour. Devilish Macbeth
By many of these trains hath sought to win me
Into his power, and modest wisdom plucks me
From over-credulous haste: but God above   120
Deal between thee and me! for even now
I put myself to thy direction, and
Unspeak mine own detraction, here abjure
The taints and blames I laid upon myself,
For strangers to my nature. I am yet   125
Unknown to woman, never was forsworn,
Scarcely have coveted what was mine own,
At no time broke my faith, would not betray
The devil to his fellow, and delight
No less in truth than life: my first false speaking 130
Was this upon myself: what I am truly,
Is thine and my poor country's to command:
Whither indeed, before thy here-approach,

Old Siward, with ten thousand warlike men,
Already at a point, was setting forth.   135
Now we'll together; and the chance of goodness
Be like our warranted quarrel! Why are you silent?
MACDUFF. Such welcome and unwelcome things at once
'Tis hard to reconcile.

Malcolm Tests Macduff   *IV.iii.1-139*

*Now whenever two Scotsmen meet, they talk of "black Mac-
beth," universally acknowledged to be "the common enemy of
man" (III.i.69). However, so corrupting is Macbeth that even his
enemies distrust each other. Macduff suffers the suspicions not
only of his wife but also, as a penalty for leaving his family, the
suspicions of his new leader, Malcolm. Hence before the counter-
Macbeth movement can defeat Macbeth, it must first unite itself.
Malcolm tests Macduff directly and indirectly. First, he directly
charges Macduff of a plot to betray him to Macbeth. Macduff
flatly denies it; "I am not treacherous." Second, Malcolm falsely
charges himself of becoming a lustful, avaricious tyrant even
worse than Macbeth. Horrified, Macduff says that such a king
would not be fit to live, let alone to govern. Throwing off his
tyrannical incognito, Malcolm is satisfied that Macduff no longer
merits distrust and is indeed a "Child of integrity," full of "good
truth and honour." Macduff will neither become a villain nor
follow a villain. With Malcolm's "black scruples" wiped out, the
opposition to Macbeth is united.*

*A major theme of the play, appearance and reality, is inverted
by Malcolm to test Macduff. Malcolm is fair but pretends to be
foul. Dissembling is used for fair purposes; virtue is covered in
order to uncover virtue. Macbeth, on the other hand, was foul
but pretended to be fair. Dissembling was used for foul purposes; vice was covered in order to destroy virtue (Duncan and
Banquo). Hypocrisy, in short, is morally neutral, depending on
its purpose. Truth is found by indirections in an immoral world.
Nor is there any a priori way to detect hypocrisy. As Duncan said
earlier, "There's no art/To find the mind's construction in the
face" (I.iv.11-12). And as Malcolm now says, "Though all things*

foul would wear the brows of grace,/Yet grace must still look so."
The only outside party that cannot be fooled by false facsimiles
of virtue is "God above," who is also an inside party. Hence Malcolm asks that "God above/Deal between thee and me!" With
God's knowledge, no incognitos are possible.

In counterfeiting foul behavior the fair Malcolm describes the
moral poles of the play in a black and white contrast between
justice and tyranny, good and evil. The first of the twelve "king-
becoming graces" is justice, serving the general interest rather
than a special interest. Malcolm's list specifically mentions three
of the four cardinal virtues (which are prudence, temperance,
fortitude, and justice), but none of the three theological virtues
(faith, hope, love). This predominance of the classical virtues
over the Christian virtues suggests a purely punitive justice, one
that punishes evil rather than absorbs evil through sacrificial
love. Evil is unilateral and external. As pure St. George slays
the dragon and frees the princess, so do pure Malcolm ("never
was forsworn") and pure Macduff ("child of integrity") slay
"black Macbeth" and free bleeding Scotland. What predomi-
nately saves the play from this melodramatic naiveté of the pure
and the dirty is that Macbeth was once pure himself. He was
once good, but his will became infinite, his desires boundless. As
Macduff says, "Boundless intemperance/In nature is a tyranny."
It is this "stanchless avarice," this "more-having" that has brought
chaos to Scotland. In falsely describing himself, Malcolm truly
describes Macbeth. "Nay, had I power, I should/Pour the sweet
milk of concord into hell,/Uproar the universal peace, confound/
All unity on earth." The ultimate end of the vulture-vice of
"Boundless intemperance" is cosmoscide. The cosmos suffers too.
In Macduff's words, "new sorrows/Strike heaven on the face, that
it resounds/As if it felt with Scotland and yell'd out/Like syllable of dolour."

If Malcolm's exposition on justice is classical, his imagery of
good and evil is Christian. He conceives of himself as a "poor
innocent lamb" and Macbeth as "Devlish Macbeth." He speaks
of angels, grace, and "God above." Likewise, Macduff speaks of
heaven and says that "Not in the legions/Of horrid hell can come
a devil more damn'd/In evils to top Macbeth." Although these

Christian references maintain the dramatic contest in black-and-white terms of God and the devil, they reflect the superhuman and subhuman dimensions of the contestants. The human act also involves divine and demonic participation. What happens in Scotland also happens in heaven and hell. The imagery reflects the final length and depth of the action. Thus we grasp the final identities of Malcolm, Macduff, and Macbeth: "Angels [Malcolm and Macduff] are bright still, though the brightest fell [Macbeth]." Although Macbeth's Christian prototype is the fallen angel Lucifer, it is Macbeth who illuminates the meaning of Lucifer, not vice versa.

(*Enter a* Doctor)

MALCOLM. Well; more anon.—Comes the king forth, I pray
    you?
                                     140

DOCTOR, Ay, sir; there are a crew of wretched souls
    That stay his cure: their malady convinces
    The great assay of art; but at his touch—
    Such sanctity hath heaven given his hand—
    They presently amend.

MALCOLM.   I thank you, doctor. (*Exit Doctor*) 145
MACDUFF. What's the disease he means?

MALCOLM.   'Tis call'd the evil:
    A most miraculous work in this good king;
    Which often, since my here-remain in England,
    I have seen him do. How he solicits heaven,
    Himself best knows: but strangely-visited people,   150
    All swoln and ulcerous, pitiful to the eye,
    The mere despair of surgery, he cures,
    Hanging a golden stamp about their necks,
    Put on with holy prayers: and 'tis spoken,
    To the succeeding royalty he leaves   155
    The healing benediction. With this strange virtue,
    He hath a heavenly gift of prophecy,
    And sundry blessings hang about his throne,
    That speak him full of grace.

The Healing Hand   *IV.iii.140-159*

Since King James I claimed the miraculous power of the royal touch to cure "the evil" (medically, scrofula), this passage is taken to be a compliment to James. Regardless of the vulgarity of the flattery or the suggestion of faith healing, this passage has thematic and structural validity. It states the problem and solution of the counter-Macbeth forces. The problem is how to overcome evil, expressed in imagery of disease (ulcerous malady) signifying the tyranny of Macbeth. As is characteristic throughout the play, disease and health images are used to express moral evil and goodness. The solution to the problem is in divine power, expressed in imagery of health and religion ("The healing benediction") signifying the "good king," either the English King (actually, Edward the Confessor) or Prince Malcolm, soon to be king of Scotland. Divine power ("holy prayers") is needed to overpower the evil Macbeth because demonic power (the witches) originally overpowered Macbeth. The ultimate source of evil is as miraculous as the ultimate source of good. It takes "this strange virtue" (the power of "healing benediction") to cure "strangely-visited people,/All swoln and ulcerous." Macbeth was certainly "strangely-visited" by the witches, but he will not be cured by any "healing benediction." So incurable is Macbeth that he would be not only the "despair of surgery" but also the despair of heaven. Because he refuses repentance and the gift of grace, Macbeth will be destroyed by "even-handed justice" (I.vii.10) instead of saved by the healing hand sanctified by heaven. Both hands, the hand of justice and the hand of grace, are instruments of heaven. Human events seem to operate on transhuman power.

(*Enter* ROSS)

MACDUFF.   See, who comes here?

MALCOLM. My countryman; but yet I know him not.   160

MACDUFF. My ever-gentle cousin, welcome hither.

MALCOLM. I know him now. Good God, betimes remove
    The means that makes us strangers!

ROSS.   Sir, amen.

MACDUFF. Stands Scotland where it did?

ROSS.   Alas, poor country!
  Almost afraid to know itself. It cannot
  Be call'd our mother, but our grave; where nothing,
  But who knows nothing, is once seen to smile;
  Where sighs and groans and shrieks that rend the air
  Are made, not mark'd; where violent sorrow seems
  A modern ecstasy: the dead man's knell   170
  Is there scarce ask'd for who; and good men's lives
  Expire before the flowers in their caps,
  Dying or ere they sicken.

MACDUFF.   O, relation
  Too nice, and yet too true!

MALCOLM.   What's the newest grief?

ROSS. That of an hour's age doth hiss the speaker: 175
  Each minute teems a new one.

MACDUFF.   How does my wife?

ROSS. Why, well.

MACDUFF.   And all my children?

ROSS.   Well too.

MACDUFF. The tyrant has not batter'd at their peace?

ROSS. No; they were well at peace when I did leave 'em.

MACDUFF. Be not a niggard of your speech: how goes 't?   180

ROSS. When I came hither to transport the tidings,
  Which I have heavily borne, there ran a rumour
  Of many worthy fellows that were out;
  Which was to my belief witness'd the rather,
  For that I saw the tyrant's power a-foot: 185
  Now is the time of help; your eye in Scotland
  Would create soldiers, make our women fight,
  To doff their dire distresses.

MALCOLM.   Be 't their comfort
  We are coming thither: gracious England hath
  Lent us good Siward and ten thousand men;   190
  An older and a better soldier none
  That Christendom gives out.

ROSS.   Would I could answer

This comfort with the like! But I have words
That would be howl'd out in the desert air,
Where hearing should not latch them.

MACDUFF. What concern they? 195
The general cause? or is it a fee-grief
Due to some single breast?

ROSS. No mind that 's honest
But in it shares some woe; though the main part
Pertains to you alone.

MACDUFF. If it be mine,
Keep it not from me, quickly let me have it. 200

ROSS. Let not your ears despise my tongue for ever,
Which shall possess them with the heaviest sound
That ever yet they heard.

MACDUFF. Hum! I guess at it.

ROSS. Your castle is surprised; your wife and babes
Savagely slaughter'd: to relate the manner, 205
Were, on the quarry of these murder'd deer,
To add the death of you.

MALCOLM. Merciful heaven!
What, man! ne'er pull your hat upon your brows;
Give sorrow words: the grief that does not speak
Whispers the o'er-fraught heart and bids it break. 210

MACDUFF. My children too?

ROSS. Wife, children, servants, all
That could be found.

MACDUFF. And I must be from thence!
My wife kill'd too?

ROSS. I have said.

MALCOLM. Be comforted:
Let 's make us medicines of our great revenge,
To cure this deadly grief. 215

MACDUFF. He has no children. All my pretty ones?
Did you say all? O hell-kite! All?
What, all my pretty chickens and their dam
At one fell swoop?

MALCOLM. Dispute it like a man.

MACDUFF. I shall do so; 220

But I must also feel it as a man:
I cannot but remember such things were,
That were most precious to me. Did heaven look on,
And would not take their part? Sinful Macduff,
They were all struck for thee! naught that I am,   225
Not for their own demerits, but for mine,
Fell slaughter on their souls. Heaven rest them now!

MALCOLM. Be this the whetstone of your sword: let grief
    Convert to anger; blunt not the heart, enrage it.

MACDUFF. O, I could play the woman with mine eyes   230
And braggart with my tongue! But, gentle heavens,
Cut short all intermission; front to front
Bring thou this fiend of Scotland and myself;
Within my sword's length set him; if he 'scape,
Heaven forgive him too!

MALCOLM.   This tune goes manly.   235
Come, go we to the king; our power is ready;
Our lack is nothing but our leave: Macbeth
Is ripe for shaking, and the powers above
Put on their instruments. Receive what cheer you may:
The night is long that never finds the day. (*Exeunt*)   240

Macduff Made Ready   *IV.iii.159-240*

Nothing happens prematurely in a Shakespearean tragedy, not even in Macbeth, *the shortest of the tragedies (only 2,108 lines long.) Despite the decisive speed of the action, there are no nontemporal shortcuts to the finale of fulfillment. All events develop painfully through the dense chronology of time to the terminating judgment of eternity, beginning in Act I with "the seeds of time" (I.iii.58) and ending in Act V with "the sear, the yellow leaf" (V.iii.23) when at last "the time is free" (V.viii.55). Paradoxically, readiness has no wings without the ballast of time.*

Here at the conclusion of Act IV time reaches its penultimate fulfillment, the readiness of the counter-Macbeth forces. This readiness takes two forms, one powerful and the other powerless. First, Malcolm borrows from "gracious England" the power of "ten thousand men," headed by "good Siward," the oldest and

*best soldier in "Christendom." Macbeth will be challenged by
the power of borrowed might from England because bleeding
Scotland has no power of its own to resist "the tyrant's power."
Secondly, the deeper form of readiness is, paradoxically, powerlessness. Before Scotland can be helped it must become helpless.
Ross's report is like news from the seventh circle of hell, the circle of violence. The dominant image of Scotland is a graveyard
where nothing smiles and only "the dea dman's knell" is heard.
Scotland "cannot/Be call'd our mother, but our grave," says Ross.
Men die "before the flowers in their caps" do. Death is the utmost point of human helplessness and finitude. It is the final discovery of powerlessness. Scotland has found herself defenseless
against Macbeth's evil strength, his evil knowledge, his evil will.
Why is human powerlessness the final form of readiness? The
answer is that only by discovering his own weakness does man
discover divine strength. The "powers above/Put on their instrument" only when the powers below become powerless. This
nexus between zero and infinity is irreducible. Macduff and Malcolm become the instruments of "the power above" only after
their own powerlessness is revealed. Neither can prevent Macbeth from murdering their dear ones. Macduff and Malcolm become armed and invulnerable but only after the outrageous
sacrifices of the innocent; "the powers above/Put on their instruments" but only after women and children are "Savagely
slaughter'd."*

*Why, we ask with Macduff, "Did heaven look on,/And would
not take their part?" Without Macduff's "mortal sword" (IV.iii.3.)
heaven has no choice; not heaven but Macduff, by leaving,
looked on "And would not take their part." Yet this explanation is
oversimplified, for it ignores the dark red fact of tragic sacrifice
as the final way of purging evil. Malcolm says of the Macduff
murders, "Let's make us medicines of our great revenge,/To cure
this deadly grief." Indeed, the medicine to cure "this deadly
grief" is made out of "deadly grief" itself. No grief, no medicine.
Scotland must become utterly broken and defeated before "Mac-
beth/Is ripe for shaking, and the powers above/Put on their instruments." Such are the inevitable, tragic requirements that must
converge and be fulfilled in time, before the counter-Macbeth*

forces can act. Anything less would be unrealistic fantasy, a sentimental lie, a shortcut to the salvation of Scotland. The finite discovers the infinite when it discovers its own finitude.

Macduff becomes unique. He is no longer merely a private revenger for his slaughtered family; he is also a public savior of bleeding Scotland. Personal anger is converted to divine wrath. If Macbeth, "this fiend of Scotland," escape "my sword's length," says Macduff, "Heaven forgive him too!" As Scotland's savior, Macduff is uniquely born by being "from his mother's womb/ Untimely ripp'd" (V.viii.15-16), a symbol of Macduff's transcendence over time. Both time and justice sanction the "great revenge" of the survivors of Duncan and Lady Macduff. Their revenge has become elevated to justice because their revenge fulfills the inevitable and untrammeled consequence of "even-handed justice" returning "To plague the inventor" of "Bloody instructions" (I.vii.1-10). Abstracted to a war of "Christendom," the conflict is between the "fiend of Scotland" and the "powers above," the demonic and the divine. Macduff's role in this war is ambivalent. In his personal involvement, he is, as a result of leaving his family, "Sinful Macduff" who seeks revenge for his slaughtered family. In his patriotic involvement, he is a "Child of integrity" (IV.iii.115) who seeks justice for his bleeding country. In both cases, personal and general, the counter-Macbeth forces can say "our power is ready," but it is a readiness that must endure the long night before it "finds the day." It is a readiness that has felt "violent sorrow" and has come through the grave.

SUMMARY OF ACT IV

POWER SHIFTS

If the power of tyranny against justice is motivated by "Vaulting ambition" (I.vii.27) and accomplished by treachery and violence, the power of justice against tyranny is motivated by "great revenge" (IV.iii.214) and accomplished by sacrifice and armed force. The mobilization of the counter-Macbeth forces is completed after Macbeth commits his last major murder. Macbeth has to run his ruthless course of power to sheer butchery, murder for murder's sake. At first he murdered men; now it is women and children. Scotland indeed has become a "grave" (IV.iii.166). It takes this extremity of suffering and sacrifice to mobilize the counter-Macbeth forces. To purge Scotland of the evil of Macbeth and Lady Macbeth costs the lives of King Duncan, Banquo, Lady Macduff, and many others. The personal cost of Macduff's killing Macbeth (in the fifth act) is the death of Lady Macduff (in the fourth). The innocent suffer injustice for the sake of justice to the guilty. In Shakespearean tragedy, the cost for a tragic victory is always sacrifice. If there is victory in the fifth act, there must be defeat in the fourth act. The power of the righteous can triumph only if the powerless innocent suffer. The gun of justice is cocked, but it takes injustice to load it. There is no justice without injustice in Shakespeare's tragic vision.

This rather outrageous tragic dialectic of power and powerlessness, of justice and injustice, cannot be explained, only described. Evil must destroy before it can be destroyed. It cannot be prevented. Evil can be overcome only at the expense of good, only by using a bloody detergent, not a golden solvent. Whenever evil is destroyed, good must be destroyed too. Such is the nature of tragic sacrifice and tragic victory. If a healthy limb is infected with gangrene, the infection is cut out only if the whole limb is cut off. Tragedy amputates good and evil together. That is why it is tragedy; otherwise, it would be cheap melodrama instead of expensive tragedy. Nor is the tragic hero without guilt. "Sinful Macduff" (IV.iii224) will kill Macbeth but only after leaving his helpless family unprotected. In fighting evil, Macduff becomes tainted with evil and cut by his own virtue. In fact, so impotent and culpable is the tragic hero that he cannot possibly win without outside help, in this case, help from England and from "the powers above" (IV.iii.238). Physical force and moral affirmation are both needed from the outside. The strength of the tragic hero grows out of the spirit's furthest reach and from the stomach's deepest hunger.

The power structure of Macbeth's world is political, moral, and cosmic. Macbeth has killed most of his enemies and has not been killed. In political force he has been stronger than the counter-Macbeth forces, although he is not all-powerful with his bloody tyranny. He has failed to kill Malcolm, Donalbain, Fleance, and Macduff. Morally, Macbeth is powerless. To become king he violates justice, the first of "the king-becoming graces" (IV.iii.91). Macbeth is morally defeated long before he is politically defeated. The counter-Macbeth forces, on the other hand, are morally powerful in their righteous revolt against a usurper who wrongs his subjects. It is morally justified to rebel against a king who rebels against justice. In direct contrast, morally and politically, are Macbeth and his enemies. Although Scotland is helpless under Macbeth's power, it amasses physical power to support its moral authority; whereas Macbeth, instead of gaining any moral authority, begins to lose his political power. A loss of right is ultimately a loss of might, and the authority of right ultimately gains might. It is now an open contest between undisguised foul and undisguised fair; no longer "Fair is foul, and foul is fair" (I.i.11).

These changing power shifts take on cosmic dimensions. The immoral Macbeth is magnified into the "fiend of Scotland" (IV.iii.233) and the moral Macduff is magnified into a "holy angel" (III.vi.45). Macduff is not actually an angel, of course, but he can do all that guardian angels can, just as Macbeth can do all that fiends from hell can. The fiend Macbeth relies on the demonic "midnight hags" (IV.i.48). Macbeth searches for security in the witches' lies. The angel Macduff, on the contrary, relies on the divine "power above." In time, the powerful fiends become powerless; justice, not tyranny, is the greatest power of the play. "Devilish Macbeth" (IV.iii.117) may "laugh to scorn/The power of man" (IV.i.79-80), but he cannot scornfully laugh off "the powers above," especially when the divine and human powers become united in the Caesarian born Macduff (V.viii.15-16). The conflict is cosmic. It is between heaven and hell, but it is fought on earth where "the evil" (IV.iii.146) is cured only if the medicine is made from "deadly grief" (IV.iii.15).

To re-emphasize, Macbeth is living in two worlds; he is losing power in the political world, and is fiercely powerless in the moral world. Villain Macbeth has murdered innocent Scotland

and is now challenged by hero Macduff (as well as by Malcolm). This elemental plot Shakespeare has interpreted for its political, moral, and cosmic values. The problem of evil is not solved by pure goodness of heart nor by sheer righteousness of force, despite the basic plot of hero versus villain. Powerless in the moral world, villain Macbeth is the immoral fiend who usurps political power; powerless in the political world, hero Macduff is the moral angel who borrows power and takes up the strength of symbolic value. The cost for mobilizing divine power against demonic power is sacrifice. Scotland will soon be a country where morality is possible once more, but there must be a tragic expiration as if heaven had disappeared (IV.iii.223-224), before the normal respiration of Scotland can resume.

ACT V

Scene I: Dunsinane. Ante-room in the castle.

Enter a Doctor of Physic *and a* Waiting-Gentlewoman.

DOCTOR. I have two nights watched with you, but can perceive no truth in your report. When was it she last walked?

GENTLEWOMAN. Since his majesty went into the field, I have seen her rise from her bed, throw her nightgown upon her, unlock her closet, take forth paper, fold it, write upon 't, read it, afterwards seal it, and again return to bed; yet all this while in a most fast sleep. 9

DOCTOR. A great perturbation in nature, to receive at once the benefit of sleep, and do the effects of watching! In this slumbery agitation, besides her walking and other actual performances, what, at any time, have you heard her say?

GENTLEWOMAN. That, sir, which I will not report after her.

DOCTOR. You may to me: and 'tis most meet you should.

GENTLEWOMAN. Neither to you nor any one, having no witness to confirm my speech. 21

(*Enter* LADY MACBETH, *with a taper*)

Lo you, here she comes! This is her very guise; and, upon my life, fast asleep. Observe her; stand close.

DOCTOR. How came she by that light?

GENTLEWOMAN. Why, it stood by her: she has light by her continually; 'tis her command.

DOCTOR. You see, her eyes are open.

GENTLEWOMAN. Ay, but their sense is shut.

DOCTOR. What is it she does now? Look, how she rubs her hands.

GENTLEWOMAN. It is an accustomed action with her, to seem thus washing her hands. I have known her continue in this a quarter of an hour.

LADY MACBETH. Yet here 's a spot.

DOCTOR. Hark! she speaks: I will set down what comes from her, to satisfy my remembrance the more strongly.   38

LADY MACBETH. Out, damned spot! out, I say!—One: two: why, then 'tis time to do 't.—Hell is murky!—Fie, my lord, fie! a soldier, and afeard? What need we fear who knows it, when none can call our power to account?—Yet who would have thought the old man to have had so much blood in him.

DOCTOR. Do you mark that?

LADY MACBETH. The thane of Fife had a wife: where is she now?— What, will these hands ne'er be clean?—No more o' that, my lord, no more o' that: you mar all with this starting.   50

DOCTOR. Go to, go to; you have known what you should not.

GENTLEWOMAN. She has spoke what she should not, I am sure of that: heaven knows what she has known.

LADY MACBETH. Here's the smell of the blood still: all the perfumes of Arabia will not sweeten this little hand. Oh, oh, oh!

DOCTOR. What a sigh is there! The heart is sorely charged.   60

GENTLEWOMAN. I would not have such a heart in my bosom for the dignity of the whole body.

DOCTOR. Well, well, well,—

GENTLEWOMAN. Pray God it be, sir.

DOCTOR. This disease is beyond my practice: yet I have known those which have walked in their sleep who have died holily in their beds.

LADY MACBETH. Wash your hands, put on your nightgown; look

not so pale.—I tell you yet again, Banquo's buried; he cannot
come out on 's grave.

DOCTOR. Even so?   72

LADY MACBETH. To bed, to bed! there's knocking at the gate:
come, come, come, come, give me your hand. What's done
cannot be undone.—To bed, to bed, to bed! (*Exit*)

DOCTOR. Will she go now to bed?

GENTLEWOMAN. Directly.

DOCTOR. Foul whisperings are abroad: unnatural deeds
Do breed unnatural troubles: infected minds   80
To their deaf pillows will discharge their secrets:
More deeds she the divine than the physician.
God, God forgive us all! Look after her;
Remove from her the means of all annoyance,
And still keep eyes upon her. So, good night: 85
My mind she has mated, and amazed my sight.
I think, but dare not speak.

GENTLEWOMAN.   Good night, good doctor. (*Exeunt*)

*In addition to the modernized Globe text just given, this scene
is printed again in the original form to offer the reader the flavor
of the text (punctuation, capitalization, spelling, stage directions)
as found in the First Folio of 1623.*

ACTUS QUINTUS   *SCENA PRIMA*

Enter a Doctor of Physicke, and a Wayting Gentlewoman.

Doct. I haue too Nights watch'd with you, but can perceiue no truth
in your report. When was it shee last walk'd?

Gent. Since his Maiesty went into the Field, I haue seene her rise from
her bed, throw her Night-Gown vpon her, vnlocke her Closset, take
foorth paper, folde it, write vpon't, read it, afterwards Seale it, and
againe returne to bed; yet all this while in a most faste sleepe.

Doct. A great perturbation in Nature, to receyue at once the benefit
of sleep, and do the effects of watching. In this slumbry agitation, besides her walking, and other actuall performances, what (at any time)
haue you heard her say?

Gent. That Sir, which I will not report after her.

Doct. You may to me, and 'tis most meet you should.

Gent. Neither to you, nor any one, hauing no witnesse to confirme my speech.   *Enter Lady, with a Taper.*
Lo you, heere she comes: This is her very guise, and vpon my life fast asleepe: obserue her, stand close.

Doct. How come she by that light?

Gent. Why it stood by her: she ha's light by her continually, 'tis her command.

Doct. You see her eyes are open.

Gent. I but their sense are shut.

Doct. What is it she do's now?
Look how she rubbes her hands.

Gent. It is an accustom'd action with her, to seeme thus washing her hands: I haue knowne her continue in this a quarter of an houre.

Lad. Yet heere's a spot.

Doct. Heark, she speaks, I will set downe what comes from her, to satisfie my remembrance the more strongly.

La. Out damned spot: out I say. One: Two: Why then 'tis time to doo't: Hell is murky. Fye, my Lord, fie, a Souldier, and affear'd? what need we feare? who knowes it, when none can call our powre to accompt: yet who would haue thought the olde man to haue had so much blood in him.

Doct. Do you marke that?

Lad. The Thane of Fife, had a wife: where is she now? What will these hands ne're be cleane: No more o'that my Lord, no more o'that: you marre all with this starting.

Doct. Go too, go too:
You haue knowne what you should not.

Gent. She ha's spoke what shee should not, I am sure of that: Heauen knowes what she ha's knowne.

La. Heere's the smell of the blood still: all the perfumes of Arabia will not sweeten this little hand. Oh, oh, oh.

Doct. What a sigh is there? The hart is·sorely charg'd.

Gent. I would not haue such a heart in my bosome for the dignity of the whole body.

Doct. Well, well, well.

Gent. Pray God it be sir.

Doct. This disease is beyond my practise: yet I haue known those which haue walkt in their sleepe, who haue dyed holily in their beds.

Lad. Wash your hands, put on your Night-Gowne, looke not so pale: I tell you againe *Banquo's* buried; he cannot come out on's graue.

Doct. Euen so?

Lady. To bed, to bed: there's knocking at the gate: Come, come, come, come, giue me your hand: What's done, cannot be vndone. To bed, to bed, to bed.

                                                            Exit Lady.

Doct. Will she go now to bed?

Gent. Directly.

Doct. Foule whisp'rings are abroad: vnnaturall deeds
Do breed vnnaturall troubles: infected mindes
To their deafe pillowes will discharge their Secrets:
More needs she the Diuine, then the Physitian:
God, God forgiue vs all. Looke after her,
Remoue from her the meanes of all annoyance,
And still keepe eyes vpon her: So goodnight,
My mind she ha's mated, and amaz'd my sight,
I thinke, but dare not speake.

Gent. Good night good Doctor.   *Exeunt.*

Sleepwalker Lady Macbeth   V.i

*Like the banquet scene (III.iv), this celebrated sleepwalking
scene is an invention of Shakespeare's not found in his sources.
The purpose of this scene, written chiefly in prose rather than
in verse in order to express a sleepwalker's incoherent speech, is
to show the final effect of the crimes, their "deepest consequence"
(I.iii.126), on Lady Macbeth. As Macbeth becomes hardened in
evil, Lady Macbeth becomes weaker. Her spiritual death in the
sleepwalking scene later drives her to her physical death
(V.vii.70-71). Mental suicide precedes physical suicide. Lighted
by only one candle, here the symbol of truth, this night scene
makes a double revelation.*

*The first revelation is to the world. Although Lady Macbeth
has consciously concealed the crime in the past, here her conscience unconsciously reveals the crime. She confesses all three
murders before two corroborating witnesses. Not only is the
crime revealed to the world, but also is it revealed to the criminal
herself. There is an internal revelation as well as an external
revelation. Lady Macbeth discovers her guilty conscience. Once
she said about the crimes, "These deeds must not be thought/
After these ways; so, it will make us mad" (II.ii.33-34). Now
she actually has become delirious. Once she said, "A little water
clears us of this deed" (II.ii.67). Now she is still washing her
hands, trying to rub out the "damned spot!" In despair she says,
"What, will these hands ne'er be clean?" Once she said, "Things
without all remedy/Should be without regard: what's done is*

done" (III.ii.11-12). Now she ironically discovers "What's done cannot be undone." Indeed, it cannot be undone; it can only be relived over and over, returning again and again to Duncan's blood, Macduff's dead wife, and Banquo's ghost. There is no escape from the torture of repetition, turning back to the nucleus of time, to the original deed, to perpetual washing. This is the Nemesis that conscience creates.

The knell that summoned Duncan "to heaven or to hell" (II.i.64) has summoned Lady Macbeth to hell. She discovers that "Hell is murky!" illuminated by the candle of her conscience. Lady Macbeth is now in hell, symbolically, and is suffering the punishments of hell. These punishments are not fire and brimstone. Instead, Lady Macbeth's "deep damnation" (I.vii.20) consists of sleepwalking in the darkness and of desperately hoping to awaken in the light. Her whole life has been lived in darkness from the moment she asked "thick night" to come "in the dunnest smoke of hell" and hide heaven in "the blanket of the dark" (I.v.51-54). And her whole life has been one of walking in her sleep from the moment Macbeth murdered "the innocent sleep" (II.ii.36). Both Macbeth and Lady Macbeth "shall sleep no more" (II.ii.43). Hell is what Lady Macbeth has made of her life, a sleepwalker in the dark. She will never awaken because "What's done cannot be undone." Lady Macbeth has come to the end of her existence; she can never return because her hands will "ne'er be clean." Such is the interior darkness that the candle illuminates to the criminal.

As in the earlier banquet scene (III.iv.), Shakespeare again uses surrealism and mock ritual to express the inner world of Lady Macbeth's spiritual destitution. Although her eyes are open, she is "in a most fast sleep" and sees nothing. Although there is no bloody spot on her hands, she sees one. Realistically, there is no spot on her hands. Surrealistically, there is a spot. Just as Macbeth's anxiety saw Banquo's ghost after he killed Banquo, so Lady Macbeth's "infected mind" sees the "damned spot" of blood on her hands after she has washed it off. The spot will not wash off because the guilt will not wash off. Lady Macbeth could cut off her hands, but that would do no good because her hands are *not guilty. Her guilt is beating in her like her heart. Ironically, she says, "What need we fear who knows it, when none can call our power to account?" Despite her demand for constant light, Lady Macbeth's own conscience calls her whole dark life to account. There is no exit from guilt, no escape from judgmental consequence, no exodus from the surrealism of the wakefulness inside sleep. "Yet who would have thought the old man to have had so much blood in him," says Lady Macbeth. He had enough to turn the green ocean red for Macbeth (II.ii.60-63) and to discolor Lady Macbeth's hands forever. Earlier Lady Macbeth had asked the "murdering ministers" to "unsex" her (I.v.41-49). For this unnatural (and symbolic) violation of nature, Lady Macbeth suffers this "great perturbation in nature" of "slumbery agitation." The doctor knows that "unnatural deeds/Do breed unnatural troubles." The true reality of this scene is surrealistic because it is the revelation of a heart "sorely charged" and of a mind diseased. Lady Macbeth's torn soul can be eased only in surrealistic hallucination, not cured by a physician. Says the doctor, aware of all men's need for forgiveness, "More she needs the divine than the physician."*

Yet the divine, even the divine touch of the king of England (IV.iii.140ff.), cannot help Lady Macbeth; for this sleepwalking scene is also a ritualistic parody of the sacrament of baptism. For Lady Macbeth the baptismal rite of purification and regeneration is a futile rite. Although she goes through the ritual of washing away sin, she cannot be cleansed and consecrated to a new life. Repentance is no longer possible. "What's done cannot be undone." Murky hell is beyond the reach of grace. Neither Christian nor non-Christian rites can help; neither washing with water nor sweetening with "all the perfumes of Arabia." Lady Macbeth's "little hand" is too colossal to wash or to perfume. Hence the rite of baptism is a parody because it is a rite performed by the damned.

This great scene of vision and recoil is one of immense illumination, like a searchlight piercing the darkness to reveal the darkness in a hell defined as the condition of spiritual death. Her life, now luminous in its deterioration, has been and will be sleep-

*walking in darkness forever. When she dies by suicide the change
to death will not be very great.*

Scene II: *The country near Dunsinane.*

Drum and colours. Enter MENTEITH, CAITHNESS, ANGUS, LENNOX,
and Soldiers.

MENTEITH. The English power is near, led on by Malcolm,
   His uncle Siward and the good Macduff:
   Revenges burn in them; for their dear causes
   Would to the bleeding and the grim alarm
   Excite the mortified man.

ANGUS.   Near Birnam wood   5
   Shall we well meet them; that way are they coming.

CAITHNESS. Who knows if Donalbain be with his brother?

LENNOX. For certain, sir, he is not: I have a file
   Of all the gentry: there is Siward's son,
   And many unrough youths that even now   10
   Protest their first of manhood.

MENTEITH.   What does the tyrant?

CAITHNESS. Great Dunsinane he strongly fortifies:
   Some say he's mad; others that lesser hate him
   Do call it valiant fury: but, for certain,
   He cannot buckle his distemper'd cause   15
   Within the belt of rule.

ANGUS.   Now does he feel
   His secret murders sticking on his hands;
   Now minutely revolts upbraid his faith-breach;
   Those he commands move only in command,
   Nothing in love: now does he feel his title   20
   Hang loose about him, like a giant's robe
   Upon a dwarfish thief.

MENTEITH.   Who then shall blame
   His pester'd senses to recoil and start,
   When all that is within him does condemn
   Itself for being there?

CAITHNESS.   Well, march we on,   25

To give obedience where 'tis truly owed:
Meet we the medicine of the sickly weal,
And with him pour we in our country's purge
Each drop of us.
LENNOX.   Or so much as it needs,
To dew the sovereign flower and drown the weeds.   30
Make we our march towards Birnam. (*Exeunt, marching*)

Macbeth's Belt and the Robe   *V.ii*

*Here the major conflict is dispassionately contrasted and ap-
praised. The conflict is Malcolm versus Macbeth: the "dear
causes" of the counter-Macbeth forces versus the "distemper'd
cause" of "the tyrant." The followers of Malcolm "give obedience
where 'tis truly owed," whereas "Those he [Macbeth] commands
move only in command,/Nothing in love." Again, in nature
imagery, it is "the sovereign flower" versus "the weeds." Nature
herself mobilizes against herself. It is likewise a conflict between
health and disease, a recurrent image in the play. "Medicine" is
needed for the "sickly weal" of Scotland to effect "our country's
purge."*

*Macbeth himself is in conflict, though his conflict is not so
nerve-shattering as is Lady Macbeth's. The "secret murders" and
the "faith-breach" of both are now known. Yet it is not this dis-
closure that makes Macbeth's "pester'd senses to recoil and start."
Macbeth long ago recognized that "We still have judgment here"
(I.vii.8). It is this irrepressible judgment that makes "all that is
within him . . . condemn/Itself for being there." The enemy of
Macbeth is Macbeth. His true self of judgment and conscience
condemns his whole rebellious being.*

*Macbeth's clothes do not even fit; they are either too small or
too large. The "borrow'd robes" (I.iii.109) of usurped authority
now "Hang loose about him, like a giant's robe/ Upon a dwarfish
thief," and the "belt of rule," he learns, "Cannot buckle his distemper'd cause." Like Dante's counterfeiters in the eighth circle
of hell who suffer from dropsy, the imposter Macbeth also suffers
from a dropsical girth. Stolen clothes, like stolen power, seldom*

fit. The robe is too big and the belt is too small. Actually, Macbeth's stature and nobility are too small and his ambition and "valiant fury" are too big. Paradoxically, Macbeth has become shrivelled with megalomania. It is hard to say which is more tormenting to Macbeth, his ridiculous wardrobe or his wicked life. Both converge in the image of the "giant's robe/Upon a dwarfish thief."

Scene III: Dunsinane. A room in the castle.

Enter MACBETH, Doctor, *and* Attendants.

MACBETH. Bring me no more reports; let them fly all:
  Till Birnam wood remove to Dunsinane,
  I cannot taint with fear. What 's the boy Malcolm?
  Was he not born of woman? The spirits that know
  All mortal consequences have pronounced me thus: 5
  "Fear not, Macbeth; no man that 's born of woman
  Shall e'er have power upon thee." Then fly, false thanes,
  And mingle with the English epicures:
  The mind I sway by and the heart I bear
  Shall never sag with doubt nor shake with fear.   10
(Enter a Servant)
  The devil damn thee black, thou cream-faced loon!
  Where got'st thou that goose look?
SERVANT. There is ten thousand—
MACBETH.   Geese, villain?
SERVANT.   Soldiers, sir.
MACBETH. Go, prick thy face, and over-red thy fear,
  Thou lily-liver'd boy. What soldiers, patch?   15
  Death of thy soul! those linen cheeks of thine
  Are counsellors to fear. What soldiers, whey-face?
SERVANT. The English force, so please you.
MACBETH. Take thy face hence. *(Exit Servant)*
                          Seyton!—I am sick at heart,
  When I behold—Seyton, I say!—This push   20
  Will cheer me ever, or disseat me now.
  I have lived long enough: my way of life

Is fall'n into the sear, the yellow leaf;
And that which should accompany old age,
As honour, love, obedience, troops of friends,   25
I must not look to have; but, in their stead,
Curses, not loud but deep, mouth-honour, breath,
Which the poor heart would fain deny, and dare not.
Seyton!
(*Enter* SEYTON)
SEYTON. What is your gracious pleasure?
MACBETH.   What news more?   30
SEYTON. All is confirm'd, my lord, which was reported.
MACBETH. I'll fight till from my bones my flesh be hack'd.
Give me my armour.
SEYTON.   'Tis not needed yet.
MACBETH. I'll put it on.
Send out moe horses; skirr the country round;   35
Hang those that talk of fear. Give me mine armour.
How does your patient, doctor?
DOCTOR.   Not so sick, my lord,
As she is troubled with thick-coming fancies,
That keep her from her rest.
MACBETH.   Cure her of that.
Canst thou not minister to a mind diseased,   40
Pluck from the memory a rooted sorrow,
Raze out the written troubles of the brain
And with some sweet oblivious antidote
Cleanse the stuff'd bosom of that perilous stuff
Which weighs upon the heart?
DOCTOR.   Therein the patient   45
Must minister to himself.
MACBETH. Throw physic to the dogs; I'll none of it.
Come, put mine armour on; give me my staff.
Seyton, send out. Doctor, the thanes fly from me.
Come, sir, dispatch. If thou couldst, doctor, cast   50
The water of my land, find her disease,
And purge it to a sound and pristine health,
I would applaud thee to the very echo,
That should applaud again.—Pull 't off, I say.—

What rhubarb, senna, or what purgative drugs, 55
Would scour these English hence? Hear'st thou of them?
DOCTOR. Ay, my good lord; your royal preparation
Makes us hear something.
MACBETH.   Bring it after me.
I will not be afraid of death and bane,
Till Birnam forest come to Dunsinane. 60
DOCTOR (*aside*). Were I from Dunsinane away and clear,
Profit again should hardly draw me here. (*Exeunt*)

Macbeth Sick at Heart   V.iii

The grand illusion of "foul is fair" (I.i.11) is now almost de-
flated. Weathering toward finality, Macbeth's "way of life/Is
fall'n into the sear, the yellow leaf." The "seeds of time" (I.iii.58)
have matured, but everything has ripened except rotten Macbeth.
Time is against Macbeth; it has not brought, as it had to the good
King Duncan, "honour, love, obedience, troops of friends." In-
stead, time has brought Macbeth "deepest consequence"
(I.iv.126), "deep damnation" (I.vii.20), "mortal consequence," and
"Curses, not loud but deep." Indeed, the original "assassination/
Could [not] trammel up the consequence" (I.vii.2-3).

Macbeth finds himself squeezed to empty desperation by the
tightening vise of "even-handed justice" (I.vii.10). The longer
Macbeth holds out, the more he feels the consequences that his
defiance of justice has created. At this stage Macbeth is "sick at
heart" and Lady Macbeth suffers from a "mind diseased." Though
Macbeth is a monster to Scotland, he never turns on his wife;
this one bond of loyalty and affection exists amidst all the violence and treachery. At this stage too, Macbeth betrays his
panicky ambivalence and blows hot and cold. He says he "cannot
taint with fear" nor "shake with fear." Yet he protests too much,
repeating the assurances of the apparitions that Birnam wood will
not move to Dunsinane. Moreover, Macbeth curses the "lily-
liver'd boy" for showing fear. "The devil damn thee black," curses
Macbeth, himself a devil. "Death of thy soul," says Macbeth
whose own soul is deathly sick. Having sold his own soul and de-

graded himself, Macbeth must in turn, in a sense, spit on some-
one else. Although Macbeth says he is unafraid, he fears fear and
would "Hang those that talk of fear." Again, Macbeth twice asks
for his armour and then pulls it off, concluding, "Bring it after
me." He is equally oscillating about the medicine to cure Lady
Macbeth's "thick-coming fancies." For mental illness the doctor
says "Therein the patient/Must minister to himself." Impatiently
Macbeth replies, "Throw physic to the dogs; I'll none of it." But
immediately he demands a further diagnosis and asks about a
"purgative drug." In his chaotic confusion, Macbeth would purge
Lady Macbeth and the advancing enemy with the same medicine.

The embracing irony of Macbeth's life is expressed in the
imagery of disease and health. Macbeth wants health, but he
persists in feeding his malady. He wants security but persists in
insecurity. He wants life but persists in death, like a person who
wants oxygen but insists on inhaling carbon monoxide. This per-
versity is as unnatural as Birnam wood moving. It is suicidal.
Everything is collapsing except Macbeth's courage, which is his
original virtue and the supreme virtue of a soldier. Yet even Macbeth's indomitable courage is no longer a virtue. He says, "I'll
fight till from my bones my flesh be hack'd." As brave and admirable as that ultimatum is, it is an affirmation in negation. It is
a statement based on scornful defiance and complete contempt
for justice and all the other "king-becoming graces" (IV.iii.91).
The only way Macbeth can affirm himself without destroying
himself is by affirming justice to begin with. Otherwise he destroys himself in trying to affirm himself; he seals his fate in defying fate.

Macbeth affirms himself in all the powers of destruction. He
now blasphemes everything, although he hedges on the witches,
his one precarious comfort. Even when he is bold with his back
against the walls of Dunsinane, he appears not courageous and
admirable, but utterly stupid. Macbeth's virtues have become
vices. Perhaps the only adequate torture for Macbeth's adamant
superman-defiance of justice is his sick rage and frustration, his
failure to become superman.

Scene IV: Country near Birnam wood.

Drum and colours. Enter MALCOLM, *old* SIWARD *and his* Son, MAC-
DUFF, MENTEITH, CAITHNESS, ANGUS, LENNOX, ROSS, *and* Soldiers,
marching.

MALCOLM. Cousins, I hope the days are near at hand
    That chambers will be safe.
MENTEITH.   We doubt it nothing.
SIWARD. What wood is this before us?
MENTEITH.   The wood of Birnam.
MALCOLM. Let every soldier hew him down a bough
    And bear 't before him: thereby shall we shadow   5
    The numbers of our host and make discovery
    Err in report of us.
SOLDIERS.   It shall be done.
SIWARD. We learn no other but the confident tyrant
    Keeps still in Dunsinane, and will endure
    Our setting down before 't.
MALCOLM.   'Tis his main hope: 10
    For where there is advantage to be given,
    Both more and less have given him the revolt,
    And none serve with him but constrained things
    Whose hearts are absent too.
MACDUFF.   Let our just censures
    Attend the true event, and put we on   15
    Industrious soldiership.
SIWARD.   The time approaches
    That will with due decision make us know
    What we shall say we have and what we owe.
    Thoughts speculative their unsure hopes relate,
    But certain issue strokes must arbitrate: 20
    Towards which advance the war. (*Exeunt, marching*)

Malcolm at Birnam Wood   *V.iv*

*Malcolm's strategy of camouflage, each soldier advancing be-
hind a bough from Birnam wood, is a fatal equivocation. Not
Birnam wood but the soldiers are moving. Yet it is the appearance*

of the moving forest that will terrify Macbeth more than the actual soldiers. The harmless wood has more might than the armed soldiers. Macbeth has used deception in the assassination of Duncan. Now Malcolm uses deception in his revenge against Macbeth. The ethics of dissembling seems to be that it is justified to deceive deceivers. Thus Macbeth used unethical deception and Malcolm uses ethical deception. However, Macbeth wraps his foul deed in a fair face ("look like the innocent flower,/But be the serpent under 't," I.v.66-67); whereas Malcolm conceals his fair deed in a fair façade. It appears that Macbeth cannot, in the drunken porter's words, "equivocate to heaven" (II.iii.11), but that heaven can equivocate to Macbeth through the righteous conspiracy of Malcolm and of nature herself. Curiously, Birnam wood is armed with soldiers, and the soldiers are armed with Birnam wood.

For special reasons, Malcolm and Macduff become the qualified guardians of Scotland: First, because of their purity; Malcolm "never was forsworn" (IV.iii.126) and Macduff, despite his wife's charge of desertion, is proved to be a "Child of integrity" (IV.iii.115). Second, because of their sacrificial loss of beloved ones, Malcolm's father and Macduff's wife and children. Third, because of their "just censures" against Macbeth's murders. "Revenges burn in them" and in all of Scotland "for their dear causes" (V.ii.3). And fourth, because of their seemingly supernatural power and superhuman deeds. Malcolm, by ordering every soldier to "hew him down a bough/And bear 't before him," causes Birnam wood to come to Dunsinane, a seemingly impossible phenomenon. Hence the power that overthrows Macbeth excels "the power of man" (IV.i.80). With Malcolm and Macduff, now like militant angels, "the powers above/Put on their instruments" (IV.iii.238-239).

Scene V: Dunsinane. Within the castle.

Enter MACBETH, SEYTON, and Soldiers, with drum and colours.

MACBETH. Hang out our banners on the outward walls:
  The cry is still "They come:" our castle's strength

Will laugh a siege to scorn: here let them lie
Till famine and the ague eat them up:
Were they not forced with those that should be ours,   5
We might have met them dareful, beard to beard,
And beat them backward home. (*A cry of women within*)
                                    What is that noise?
SEYTON. It is the cry of women, my good lord. (*Exit*)
MACBETH. I have almost forgot the taste of fears:
The time has been, my senses would have cool'd   10
To hear a night-shriek; and my fell of hair
Would at a dismal treatise rouse and stir
As life were in 't: I have supp'd full with horrors;
Direness, familiar to my slaughterous thoughts,
Cannot once start me.

Macbeth's Gluttony   V.v.1-15

Although Macbeth may "Hang out our banners on the outward walls" and "laugh a siege to scorn," inside there is no laughter. His nerves jaded, Macbeth is now hardened to horror. The imagery of eating reveals indirectly the cause and nature of Macbeth's shock-proof nerves and numbed senses. The three references to eating ("eat," "taste," and "supp'd") all express a natural appetite. Yet Macbeth perverts this natural appetite into an excessive and unnatural gluttony. Macbeth's uncontrolled appetite has "supp'd full with horrors." Instead of eating food, he unnaturally sups horrors and tastes fears. He clearly has been eating at the witches' cauldron, not at the banquet table. Macbeth radically reverses nature by having famine gorge instead of starve, thus destroying life. Perhaps the subliminal horror revealed here is cannibalism since the objects of Macbeth's murderous gluttony are human lives. If Lady Macbeth unnaturally suffers from wakefulness inside a sleep, Macbeth unnaturally suffers from starvation inside satiety.

(*Re-enter* SEYTON)
                          Wherefore was that cry?   15
SEYTON. The queen, my lord, is dead.

MACBETH. She should have died hereafter;
There would have been a time for such a word.
To-morrow, and to-morrow, and to-morrow,
Creeps in this petty pace from day to day   20
To the last syllable of recorded time,
And all our yesterdays have lighted fools
The way to dusty death. Out, out, brief candle!
Life's but a walking shadow, a poor player
That struts and frets his hour upon the stage   25
And then is heard no more: it is a tale
Told by an idiot, full of sound and fury,
Signifying nothing.

Macbeth's Epitaph   V.v.15-28

In rich, magnificent poetry, this great speech summarizes Mac-
beth's empty, meaningless life. Macbeth is reciting his epitaph,
an epitaph which concludes that life is not worth living. All illu-
sions about "the swelling act/Of the imperial theme" (I.iii.128-
129) and about "sovereign sway and masterdom" (I.v.71) have
collapsed. Macbeth now faces his last illusion—disillusion. Life
is "a tale/Told by an idiot, full of sound and fury,/Signifying
nothing."

Here is the immobile end of all the inevitable, creeping to-
morrows. Here, in rigid emptiness, is the static dead end. Time
has transfixed Macbeth, like a movie film stopping in the next-
to-the-last frame. For Macbeth, the "deepest consequence" (I.iii.
126) of "deep damnation" (I.vii.20) is death before death, the
death of all values and meaning. Everything signifies nothing,
and, as Macbeth anticipated earlier, "nothing is/But what is
not" (I.iii.141-142). No matter what tomorrows or the next minute
brings, Macbeth's life is final and formed in a frigid, formless
world of darkness. To have once had "Golden opinions from all
sorts of people" (I.vii.33) and now to have sold them for isolated
darkness is pure idiotism. Only a qualified idiot has the right to
say life is "full of sound and fury/Signifying nothing." Macbeth
has the right. He speaks as if he had murdered himself and were
now attending his own funeral. Although Macbeth continues to
draw breath and go through the motions of existence, he knows

he has nothing serious to think about, not even his survival. Macbeth is not going anywhere, not even to hell. He is already there, for hell is a condition that may be found in any place. (In the orthodoxy of Dante's world Macbeth's literal damnation would begin at death because hell is literally the state of souls after death and allegorically the state of souls in life.) In any event, spiritual death, both for Macbeth and Lady Macbeth, precedes physical death.

On learning his queen is dead, Macbeth says, "She should have died hereafter." Sooner or later would make little difference to one who has wasted all her yesterdays in sterile folly. Lady Macbeth dies (suicide, V.viii.70-71) as she lived (unsexed, I.v.42) —both unnaturally. Macbeth appears to take the news indifferently; perhaps it is too heavy for his sense to seize. The castle is empty and Macbeth is alone without his "dear wife" (III.ii.36), his "dearest chuck" (III.ii.45).

The central image in these dozen lines is the candle, thematically expressing time and symbolically the light of truth. The burning candle measures man's life, but more significantly illuminates its meaning. Both the candle here and the candle Lady Macbeth held in the sleepwalking scene reveal "Life's but a walking shadow." In both of these scenes of revelation it takes a candle to reveal the darkness. Paradoxically, the illumination is darkness, the realization that foul is not fair. Now that Macbeth is full of his own fate, this revelation is fully apparent and fully found. To ease the ennui Macbeth says, "Out, out, brief candle!" This nihilistic outcry against his bankrupt life comes out of the heart as well as the head. Extinguishing a flickering candle butt becomes a futile gesture after one has extinguished the stars. Long ago Macbeth had said, "Stars, hide your fires;/Let not light see my black and deep desires" (I.iv.50-51). Banquo himself observed on the night of Duncan's murder that "in heaven" the "candles are all out" (II.i.5). Macbeth's life is now "a walking shadow" because long ago he had divested the heavens of their stars. In doing so, Macbeth had to turn traitor to his true nature, which was "too full o' the milk of human kindness" (I.v.18), usurp false robes, and play the hypocrite. Hence his life has been inauthentic, "a poor player/That struts

*and frets his hour upon the stage/And then is heard no more."
Time and truth converge in the symbol of the burning candle.
What happens in the "petty pace" of creeping time signifies Macbeth's salvation or damnation. After Duncan's assassination,
Macbeth had confessed, "from this instant,/There's nothing serious in mortality" (II.iii.98). The "mortal consequences" (V.ii.5)
of that instant have been "a tale/Told by an idiot, full of sound
and fury,/Signifying nothing." Macbeth, therefore, travels on two
paths, one chronological and one moral, one temporal and one
eternal. On the night of Duncan's murder, when the bell struck
at two, Lady Macbeth said, "Why, then 'tis time to do 't" (V.i.40).
For Macbeth, it was a "summons . . . to heaven or to hell"
(II.i.64). Macbeth's footsteps turned out to be a map of hell.*

*Macbeth's life is a record of accumulated idiotism and nihilism,
ending in the final consummation of isolation and meaninglessness. Yet ironically, this chaos would be impossible without an
ordered cosmos governed by "even-handed justice" (I.vii.10).
Were there not a built-in meaning and value, meaninglessness
would be impossible. Macbeth can destroy meaning but cannot
prevent meaninglessness. He can blow out the candle, but then
"Life's but a walking shadow." Consequences cannot be cheated,
as Macbeth's entire life testifies. The revenge, as it were, of a
well-tuned instrument on its ruthless destroyer is "sound and
fury,/Signifying nothing." Meaninglessness is its own Nemesis.
As long as meaninglessness is meaningless, the structure of meaning cannot be destroyed. Paradoxically, Macbeth's empty life
and Duncan's full life are equal proofs of a structured universe
of order and justice. No star is safely extinguished. In these final
thoughts on human destiny Macbeth admits the truth of his life
in which there is no other meaning than "sound and fury,/Signi-
fying nothing." The candle is out and Macbeth is in the dark
forever. Indeed, "the be-all and the end-all [is] here,/But here,
upon this bank and shoal of time"; there is no "life to come"
(I.vii.5-7).*

MACBETH *(cont'd)*

(Enter a Messenger)
    Thou comest to use thy tongue; thy story quickly.

MESSENGER. Gracious my lord,   30
   I should report that which I say I saw,
   But know not how to do it.
MACBETH.   Well, say, sir.
MESSENGER. As I did stand my watch upon the hill,
   I look'd toward Birnam, and anon, methought,
   The wood began to move.
MACBETH.   Liar and slave!   35
MESSENGER. Let me endure your wrath, if 't be not so:
   Within this three mile may you see it coming;
   I say, a moving grove.
MACBETH.   If thou speak'st false,
   Upon the next tree shalt thou hang alive,
   Till famine cling thee: if thy speech be sooth,   40
   I care not if thou dost for me as much.
   I pull in resolution, and begin
   To doubt the equivocation of the fiend
   That lies like truth: "Fear not, till Birnam wood
   Do come to Dunsinane:" and now a wood   45
   Comes toward Dunsinane. Arm, arm, and out!
   If this which he avouches does appear,
   There is nor flying hence nor tarrying here.
   I 'gin to be aweary of the sun,
   And wish the estate o' the world were now undone.   50
   Ring the alarum-bell! Blow, wind! come, wrack!
   At least we'll die with harness on our back. (*Exeunt*)

Birnam Wood Comes to Dunsinane   *V.v.29-52*

*For Macbeth the impossible happens; Birnam Wood comes
to Dunsinane. This miracle, a combination of low trickery and
high symbolism, exposes to Macbeth "the equivocation of the
fiend/That lies like truth." It further shows nature participating
in the retribution of Macbeth's crimes as the earth had earlier
participated in the suffering (II.iv). Just as Macbeth turned
against nature, including his own, so nature becomes unnatural
and turns against Macbeth. Macbeth's butchery is no more anti-
natural than "a moving grove." Apparently, Scotland, England,*

the witches, the "powers above" (IV.iii.238), and nature herself are all against Macbeth. When Macbeth says, "I 'gin to be aweary of the sun," he is saying he is tired of life (the sun's heat), of truth (the sun's light), and of the crown (the sun as king of the planets).

Despite certain death, Macbeth's spirit is indomitable. Although his power is powerless, his will is adamant. He knows his armour is useless, but "At least we'll die with harness on our back." Macbeth commands his men to "Ring the alarum-bell!" even though he knows this time it does not ring for Duncan (II.i.62-64).

Scene VI: *Dunsinane. Before the castle.*

Drum and colours. Enter MALCOLM, *old* SIWARD, MACDUFF, *and their* Army, *with boughs.*

MALCOLM. Now near enough: your leavy screens throw down,
And show like those you are. You, worthy uncle,
Shall, with my cousin, your right-noble son,
Lead our first battle: worthy Macduff and we
Shall take upon's what else remains to do,   5
According to our order.
SIWARD.   Fare you well.
Do we but find the tyrant's power to-night,
Let us be beaten, if we cannot fight.
MACDUFF. Make all our trumpets speak; give them all breath,
Those clamorous harbingers of blood and death. (*Exeunt*) 10

Macduff's Trumpets of Death   *V.vi*

Malcolm orders his soldiers to drop their "leavy screens" and reveal themselves. Supernatural appearance gives way to the natural reality of armed soldiers. Seeming divine power becomes real human power. This transformation is announced by trumpets, "Those clamorous harbingers of blood and death." Like the earlier "trumpet-tongued" angels that sounded the "deep damnation" (I.vii.19-20) of Duncan's murderer, Malcolm's trumpets

*again sound the final judgment of Macbeth. If drums announce
Macbeth's temptation by the witches (I.iii.30), trumpets announce
Macbeth's judgment by the angels.*

Scene VII. *Another part of the field.*

Alarums. Enter MACBETH.

MACBETH. They have tied me to a stake; I cannot fly,
But, bear-like, I must fight the course. What's he
That was not born of woman? Such a one
Am I to fear, or none.
(*Enter young* SIWARD)
YOUNG SIWARD. What is thy name?
MACBETH.   Thou 'lt be afraid to hear it. 5
YOUNG SIWARD. No; though thou call'st thyself a hotter name
Than any is in hell.
MACBETH.   My name's Macbeth.
YOUNG SIWARD. The devil himself could not pronounce a title
More hateful to mine ear.
MACBETH.   No, nor more fearful.
YOUNG SIWARD. Thou liest, abhorred tyrant; with my sword   10
I'll prove the lie thou speak'st. (*They fight and young* SIWARD
is slain)
MACBETH.   Thou wast born of woman.
But swords I smile at, weapons laugh to scorn,
Brandish'd by man that's of a woman born. (*Exit*)
(*Alarums. Enter* MACDUFF)
MACDUFF.That way the nóise is. Tyrant, show thy face!
If thou be'st slain and with no stroke of mine,   15
My wife and children's ghosts will haunt me still.
I cannot strike at wretched kerns, whose arms
Are hired to bear their staves: either thou, Macbeth,
Or else my sword with an unbatter'd edge
I sheathe again undeeded. There thou shouldst be;   20
By this great clatter, one of greatest note
Seems bruited. Let me find him, fortune!
And more I beg not. (*Exit. Alarums*)

(*Enter* MALCOLM *and old* SIWARD)

SIWARD. This way, my lord; the castle's gently render'd:
 The tyrant's people on both sides do fight;   25
 The noble thanes do bravely in the war;
 The day almost itself professes yours,
 And little is to do.

MALCOLM.   We have met with foes
 That strike beside us.

SIWARD.   Enter, sir, the castle. (*Exeunt. Alarums*)

Macbeth Kills Young Siward   *V.vii*

 Macbeth, identified with images of beasts ("bear-like") and demons ("devil"), easily slays young Siward and feels confidently invincible. On the other hand, old Siward, finding little resistance in Macbeth's defecting soldiers, easily takes Macbeth's castle and feels confidently victorious. The complacency on both sides is ironic. Macbeth is not yet aware of Macduff's untimely birth (V.viii.15), and old Siward is not yet aware of his son's untimely death. To purge the evil of the bestial, demonic Macbeth demands bloody sacrifice (young Siward, as well as Lady Macduff and Duncan) and supernatural (Birnam Wood) and superhuman (Macduff) powers.

Scene VIII: Another part of the field.

Enter MACBETH.

MACBETH. Why should I play the Roman fool, and die
 On mine own sword? whiles I see lives, the gashes
 Do better upon them.

(*Enter* MACDUFF)

MACDUFF.   Turn, hell-hound, turn!

MACBETH. Of all men else I have avoided thee:
 But get thee back; my soul is too much charged   5
 With blood of thine already.

MACDUFF.   I have no words:
 My voice is in my sword: thou bloodier villain

Than terms can give thee out! (*They fight*)

MACBETH.   Thou losest labour:
As easy mayst thou the intrenchant air
With thy keen sword impress as make me bleed: 10
Let fall thy blade on vulnerable crests;
I bear a charmed life, which must not yield
To one of woman born.

MACDUFF.   Despair thy charm;
And let the angel whom thou still hast served
Tell thee, Macduff was from his mother's womb   15
Untimely ripp'd.

MACBETH. Accursed be that tongue that tells me so,
For it hath cow'd my better part of man!
And be these juggling fiends no more believed,
That palter with us in a double sense;   20
That keep the word of promise to our ear,
And break it to our hope. I'll not fight with thee.

MACDUFF. Then yield thee, coward,
And live to be the show and gaze o' the time:
We'll have thee, as our rarer monsters are,   25
Painted upon a pole, and underwrit,
"Here may you see the tyrant."

MACBETH.   I will not yield,
To kiss the ground before young Malcolm's feet,
And to be baited with the rabble's curse.
Though Birnam wood be come to Dunsinane,   30
And thou opposed, being of no woman born,
Yet I will try the last. Before my body
I throw my warlike shield. Lay on, Macduff,
And damn'd be him that first cries "Hold, enough!"

                              (*Exeunt, fighting. Alarums*)

Macbeth Meets Macduff   *V.viii.1-34*

*Macbeth's final hour is hardly one of confession, repentance,
and red wine. Rather it is one of disenchantment, resolution, and
perdition. The invincible Macbeth at last encounters the one
invulnerable man, Macduff, and Macbeth is no longer invincible.*

He says he bears "a charmed life," but Macduff, who was "from his mother's womb/Untimely ripp'd," replies, "Despair thy charm." Macbeth now shudders; his charmed life was not really charmed. Macbeth's trust in his seeming invulnerability is his most vulnerable point. Long ago, just before Macbeth met the witches on the heath, they said, "Peace! the charm's wound up" (I.iii.37). (Were Macbeth not blinded by his own imperial ambitions, the charm, of course, could not have bewitched Macbeth.) This magical charm, the immense deception of Macbeth, is at last unwound in a dazzling discovery of despair. The witches prophesied victory, not defeat; invulnerability, not vulnerability. Now there is no security and no protection; success has turned out to be failure. The charm was a lie; the witches cheaters. Their victim now enlightened to the dark deception, the "juggling fiends" will "palter" no more with Macbeth "in a double sense." With the witches' final equivocation revealed, Macbeth's perplexed destiny is now unperplexed.

Macbeth is conquered, but only half-conquered. Despite the fact that his knowledge turned out to be ignorance; his wisdom, folly; and his power, impotence; despite the discovery that he is a "dwarfish thief" in a "giant's robe" (V.ii.21-22); nevertheless Macbeth's stubborn will never yields. He obstinately refuses "To kiss the ground before young Malcolm's feet" and tenaciously fights on his own after all help and hope have deserted him. "I will not yield. . . . Yet I will try the last. . . . Lay on, Macduff,/ And damn'd be him that first cries 'Hold, enough!'" Macbeth is intransigent. Macduff can cut off Macbeth's head, but he cannot bend the bodiless half of Macbeth, his adamant will. The body, not the soul of tyranny, is destroyed. In the face of certain destruction, Macbeth's fighting spirit is indestructible. The soldier who dies fighting understands Macbeth's deathless will. Demonic though he is in his self-willed defiance, Macbeth has the heroic spirit that cuts into life. At this point, Macduff is hardly a hero; he cannot lose. Macbeth can and does. Yet he affirms himself, even though there will be no Macbeth and no hope for Macbeth. Such desperate self-affirmation in negation may be a madman's death-wish, or it may be an admirable display of spiritual courage. A fundamental value judgment must be made here. Macbeth's valor was heroic when, "Disdaining fortune, with his brandish'd steel" (I.ii.17), Macbeth was fighting Scotland's enemies. However, still "Disdaining fortune," Macbeth's valor is demonic when he is fighting Scotland herself. Clearly valor is of neutral moral value until evaluated by justice and loyalty. Macbeth's valor turns immoral by supporting treason and tyranny. Amorally, Macbeth's fighting spirit is heroic and admirable; morally, it is demonic and hateful. Macbeth himself so reverses his moral values that submission to morality is to be damned. "And damn'd be him that first cries 'Hold, enough!'" Macbeth dies a moral eccentric; surrender is damnation. Macbeth could have died in repentance as did the first thane of Cawdor (see commentary, I.iv.1-14) or he could have wasted away into suicide as did Lady Macbeth (V.i). His pride, like pain torturing itself, forbid's both.

Since Macbeth can violate nature by murder and tyranny, nature must become unnatural to become invulnerable to Macbeth. Hence Macbeth's Nemesis, moving Birnam wood and Macduff's miraculous birth, is nature self-transcended, a power over nature; symbolically, the supernatural. Because Macbeth the "hell-hound" allied himself with the demonic powers of "the juggling fiends," it takes divine or superhuman powers to defeat him. Macduff is the weapon of the sublime from which Macbeth shrinks.

Macbeth's heart is a rock that cannot be broken. This is why there is permanent damnation with no hope. Despite a "Soul . . . . too much charged/With blood," neither remorse nor a jackhammer can crack Macbeth's heart. He dies preserved by his own icy heart, a heart frozen by the terrible deeds he has done and hardened from the suffering of what he has done. As Lady Macbeth's life was a wakefulness inside a sleep, so Macbeth's life has been an affirmation inside a negation. The capital irony of this destitute life is that Macbeth sends no one to hell but himself.

(*Retreat. Flourish. Enter, with drum and colours,* MALCOLM, *old* SIWARD, ROSS, *the other* Thanes, *and* Soldiers)

MALCOLM. I would the friends we miss were safe arrived.   35

SIWARD. Some must go off: and yet, by these I see,
  So great a day as this is cheaply bought.
MALCOLM. Macduff is missing, and your noble son.
ROSS. Your son, my lord, has paid a soldier's debt:
  He only lived but till he was a man;   40
  The which no sooner had his prowess confirm'd
  In the unshrinking station where he fought,
  But like a man he died.
SIWARD.   Then he is dead?
ROSS. Ay, and brought off the field: your cause of sorrow
  Must not be measured by his worth, for then   45
  It hath no end.
SIWARD.   Had he his hurts before?
ROSS. Ay, on the front.
SIWARD.   Why then, God's soldier be he!
  Had I as many sons as I have hairs,
  I would not wish them to a fairer death:
  And so, his knell is knoll'd.
MALCOLM.   He's worth more sorrow,   50
  And that I'll spend for him.
SIWARD.   He's worth no more:
  They say he parted well, and paid his score:
  And so, God be with him! Here comes newer comfort.

Old Siward's Loss   *V.vii.35-53*

The final sacrifice is made by old Siward, who loses his son to bloody Macbeth. No matter what Siward Senior says, no victory over evil is "cheaply bought." The cost is innocent lives and tragic waste. Any elegy commemorating the dead victims of Macbeth must recognize that there is more in a man than mortality. There is the infinite value of one human being, in this case young Siward, who "must not be measured by his worth, for then/ It hath no end." Human life cannot be weighed despite all mortality. An equally intangible value is how a man dies despite death. Young Siward, "God's soldier," "parted well, and paid his score" with "his hurts . . . on the front." Bravely, "like a man he died." A cowardly death betrays a cowardly life. Young Siward lived a courageous life because he died courageously. Macbeth's

*sword can destroy young Siward, but Macbeth's evil cannot in-
jure him; the lad's virtue guards him. Socrates was right; no evil
can befall a good man. Hence old Siward, the oldest and best
soldier in "Christendom" (IV.iii.191-192), would not wish his dead
son "a fairer death." Regardless, all comfort in death is cold comfort; the sorrow sticks until gradually forgotten.*

(*Re-enter* MACDUFF, *with* MACBETH's *head*)

MACDUFF. Hail, king! for so thou art: behold, where stands
   The usurper's cursed head: the time is free:　　　　　　55
   I see thee compass'd with thy kingdom's pearl,
   That speak my salutation in their minds;
   Whose voices I desire aloud with mine:
   Hail, King of Scotland!

ALL.　　　　　　　　　　Hail, King of Scotland! (*Flourish*)

MALCOLM. We shall not spend a large expense of time　　　60
   Before we reckon with your several loves,
   And make us even with you. My thanes and kinsmen,
   Henceforth be earls, the first that ever Scotland
   In such an honour named. What's more to do,
   Which would be planted newly with the time,　　　65
   As calling home our exiled friends abroad
   That fled the snares of watchful tyranny;
   Producing forth the cruel ministers
   Of this dead butcher and his fiend-like queen,
   Who, as 'tis thought, by self and violent hands　　　70
   Took off her life; this, and what needful else
   That calls upon us, by the grace of Grace,
   We will perform in measure, time and place:
   So, thanks to all at once and to each one,
   Whom we invite to see us crown'd at Scone. (*Flourish.
   Exeunt*)　　　　　　　　　　　　　　75

The New King Malcolm　　　　　　　　　　V.viii.54-75

   *The final cadence of the play resolves death into rebirth. The
death of old tyranny is expressed by Macbeth's decapitated head;*

it was "The usurper's cursed head," his evil brain, not his body or hands, that was the root of the rebellion. With the death of "this dead butcher and his fiend-like queen," the years of "watchful tyranny" are ended and "the time is free." A new time of justice, order, and peace is reborn. "Time and the hour [have run] through the roughest day" (I.iii.147). The "seeds of time" (I.iii.58) have ripened and brought forth the new King Malcolm, and the scythe of time has become sharpened and cut down the old king Macbeth. Time is Scotland's hope and Macbeth's despair. The "deepest consequence" (I.iii.126) of time is death for Macbeth and rebirth for Scotland.

It is a rebirth, not merely a birth, because Duncan's son Malcolm resumes his father's command of the kingdom and, "by the grace of Grace," restores justice to Scotland. In "calling home our exiled friends abroad" (his brother Donalbain included), Malcolm reunites the divided land of Scotland. Morality is possible once more. Fair is no longer foul, and the red ocean is green again (II.ii.61-63). The weather changes and a clearness has returned. The "fog and filthy air" (I.i.12) have blown away; the air grows fresh to breathe after a long "thick night" palled "in the dunnest smoke of hell" (I.v.51-52). Duncan had wanted to "plant" Macbeth and make him "full of growing" (I.iv.28-29), but Macbeth and Lady Macbeth became malignant "weeds" (V.ii.30) and had to be deracinated. With the death of the old evils, "The time is free" and fresh seeds of life may be "planted newly with the time."

Lest this last transparence of restored purity seem too sanguine, the picture is not without its sanguinary shadows of things to come. Macbeth has been destroyed but not the witches, who had promised to meet again "When the hurly burly's done/ When the battle's lost and won" (I.i.3-4). The witches meet after all battles, not only after Macbeth's defeat of Macdonwald and Norway (I.ii), but also after Malcolm's defeat of Macbeth. Now the hurly-burly is done; Macbeth has won and lost. The witches are now awaiting their next victim, winding up their charm again to tempt another soul with ambition. Who will it be? Macbeth killed Duncan's enemies; Macduff has killed Malcolm's enemy. Duncan promoted Macbeth to thane of Cawdor before he met

*the witches. Malcolm now promotes all his thanes to earls. Which
one of these newly planted earls will, like Duncan's earlier de-
fender, the newly planted Macbeth, now meet the fatal witches?
Since we are completely outside the frame of the play, the question is irrelevant and the answer impossible. Nevertheless, Shakespeare's exacting sense of irony would find only one man now
qualified to enact all over again the timeless story of the revolt
and fall of Lucifer. . . . Peace is a war that never ends because
the only permanence for man is the possibility of recreation or
destruction beginning again.*

SUMMARY OF ACT V

MACBETH DAMNED AND SCOTLAND PURGED

The last line of Act IV reads, "The night is long that never
finds the day" (IV.iii.240). In Act V the day is found but only for
Scotland, not for Macbeth or Lady Macbeth. For them, the night
is eternal. Though buried only once, they die twice: the second
time by decapitation and by suicide; the first time by sickness of
heart (V.iii.19) and by "a mind diseased" (V.iii.40). Their lives
are prophetically and ironically fulfilled in this last act. In Act
I Lady Macbeth had said, "Come, thick night . . . in the dunnest
smoke of hell" (I.v.51-52). By Act V it does come as a profound
inner darkness. While fast asleep she discovers that "Hell is
murky!" (V.i.40). In Act I Macbeth is described killing the
"merciless Macdonwald" (I.ii.9) and fixing "his head upon our
battlements" (I.ii.23). Macduff does the same for Macbeth in
Act V. The crowning irony is the crown itself. Macbeth's "Vaulting ambition" (I.vii.27) is to possess the "golden round" (I.v.29).
This king-wish comes true, ironically true. Hell, symbolically, is
a state of the loss of the good of the intellect and the possession
of a permanently rebel will. With his blinded intellect and his
intransigent will, Macbeth becomes king, the king of hell. Macbeth's ambition was to be king; his punishment is to become
king.

It is "even-handed justice" (I.vii.10) that makes these ironic
fulfillments possible, and prevents Macbeth from literally getting

away with murder. This inescapable justice is transcendent because "the powers above/Put on their instruments" (V.iii.238-239) to fulfill it. Justice must rest on an unconditional structure of power to prevent the conditional powers of men like Macbeth from usurping justice with tyrannical ambition. Justice trespasses on those that trespass on it. All mortal actions are judged by the "knell/That summons . . . to heaven or to hell" (II.i.64). Hence all mortal actions that try to defy or to circumvent that judgmental summons are ironic. With "Vaulting ambition" (I.vii.27), Macbeth can make himself king, but he cannot make himself just. Thus deprived of justice, "the first of the king-becoming graces" (IV.iii.91-92), Macbeth becomes king of hell. The logic of evil is "To catch the nearest way" (I.v.19), but the end of evil is found in a profounder logic. Macbeth destroys himself in trying to affirm himself. He loses his head to gain a crown. So inverted and invincible is Macbeth's will that he sacrifices himself to himself. Affirmation in negation is self-destruction. It is also idiotism. Macbeth is left helpless where he began, "here, upon this bank and shoal of time" (I.vii.5), a place in which to be is not enough to be, a place "cabin'd, cribb'd, confined" (III.iv.24). For Macbeth, it is an ever-shrinking, ever-darkening world.

With the poison in its blood purged by the counter-Macbeth forces, Scotland will be an ever-brightening world. To free the time of Macbeth's tyranny has required the symbolic superhuman power of a man who could not be wounded, Macduff. Equally necessary, however, have been the lives of those who could be slaughtered, Duncan, Banquo, Lady Macduff, and young Siward. In their blood and on Macduff's angelic sword malignant evil dies. Both tragic sacrifice and miraculous birth point to the ultimate power that overthrows the demonic Macbeth, a power Malcolm names "The grace of Grace" (V.viii.72). The ironic pattern of the play moves from creation through destruction to damnation for Macbeth. "Light thickens" (III.ii.50). The tragic pattern of the play moves from creation through destruction to recreation for Scotland. With "The instruments of darkness" (I.iii.124) to guide him, Macbeth loses; and "with Him above/To ratify the work" (III.vi.32-33), "the battle's lost and won" (I.i.3-4); "the time is free" (V.viii.55).

CONCLUSION

SELF-DESTRUCTION OF A GOOD MAN

After our reading of *Macbeth*, it should be clear that the play is the story of an immoral man in a moral universe. When magnified *sua voluntate*, that is, to "His will" (Dante, *Paradiso*, Canto III), it is a conflict between man's will and the divine will. Macbeth lives in a structured world of fixed values, particularly the values of good and evil, of fair and foul, of tyranny and justice. His freedom deteriorating into self-will, Macbeth challenges this structured world and loses. In attempting to destroy all references, Macbeth destroys himself. Hence the meaning of his life is meaningless, or ironic. Symbolically, it is hell—"a tale/ Told by an idiot, full of sound and fury,/Signifying nothing" (V.v.26-28).

The direction and movement of the play may be plotted along a course similar to that of a freely swinging pendulum. The pendulum, hanging straight down between the right and left quadrants in an equilibrium position of rest, may be taken as "even-handed justice" (I.vii.10), the moral center of the play. Let us say that when the pendulum swings to the right, the action is just; when it swings to the left, it is unjust. Thus a right swing is a positive moral displacement on the side of justice and good, and a left swing is a negative moral displacement on the side of injustice and evil. Macbeth, of course, would mask these structural values by making foul appear fair. In Act I the witches say, "Peace! the charm's wound up" (I.iii.37). With this bewitching shove, Macbeth begins his momentous swing from the right quadrant to the left. With each murder the pendulum gathers momentum and makes a deeper displacement into the negative quadrant. It reaches the top of its arc with the murder of Lady Macduff and her children. As he goes deeper into blood, Macbeth's moral power decreases; but, with fine economy, the moral power of the counter-Macbeth forces increases. Now the moment is ripe for the return swing, the restoration of Scotland to justice. When the pendulum swings back toward the right quadrant and settles at the original equilibrium position, then "the time is free" (V.viii.55). Justice has replaced tyranny. Macbeth rides up on the left and down on the right, ending in isolation and emptiness. The counter-Macbeth forces ride down on the left and up on the right, ending in reunion and freedom. Thus the dominant direction of the play is from right to left, from justice to tyranny. Left is the direction of irony. It brings self-defeat instead of self-fulfillment as expected. Macbeth gains the crown but loses his head. He gains everything but has nothing. Hence the proverb, "The devil is an ass." The turning point or climax of the play comes in Act V when the pendulum reaches its negative peak and, weighted with the moral outrage of the counter-Macbeth forces, sweeps back down in a return to order and justice. Another swing of the pendulum to the left would be another story.

This simplified metaphor of the dramatic action of the play makes clear that Macbeth lives in a structured world of positive and negative values, a world where every action involves a relationship, where to be is to be of worth. It is a world where the values of existence precede existence, where a man can make himself king by ambition but cannot, by ambition, make himself just. Macbeth stole the crown, but he could not steal justice along with it. Ironically, Duncan is still king, even after he is murdered. Both justice and judgment existed before Macbeth; he cannot invent what should be out of what is. The worth of life cannot be adequately measured by any man, for, like old Siward's sorrow, "It hath no end" (V.viii.45-46). Macbeth knows that we "still have judgement here" (I.vii.8) and that judgment cannot be circumvented. There is no exit from this essence preceding existence, from this judgment and justice that expresses itself in the untrammeled consequence of the falling pendulum.

Unlike the modern existentialist who would create meaning in the face of meaninglessness, Macbeth would destroy meaning and "Uproar the universal peace, confound/All unity on earth" (IV.iii.99-100). The modern existentialist, we will assume, did not make his meaningless world, but Macbeth did make his. Herein lies the double dignity of Shakespeare's vision of man and his world. Man is free in an ordered universe; he is free to choose but not free from the consequences. He can defy the order, but he cannot defeat it. Radically stated, Macbeth has dignity because he is free to damn and to destroy himself. Had he not this freedom, he would be a puppet, not a man. And had the "powers above" (IV.iii.238) not taken enough interest in him to punish him, he would be a cypher, not a man. Thus the double dignity of man in Shakespeare's vision: man is free to choose his final destiny, whether it be empty or full; and his universe is concerned, not indifferent; it punishes and rewards with "even-handed justice" (I.vii.10). The pendulum is free and can be displaced, but it always returns, though dripping with blood, to the position of equilibrium. As bloody as Scotland becomes, it is still a correct catastrophe. Chaos has a cause, and cosmos has the last word. Macbeth wanted to be the highest man in Scotland with nothing higher than himself. This desperado-desire is ironic because irony is possible only if there is a reference higher than the highest man.

We have further seen throughout the play that the imagery changes as the pendulum swings. Dramatic action in the right quadrant of justice is accompanied by positive imagery of light, health, and peaceful nature. However, as the pendulum displaces into the left quadrant of tyranny, "Light thickens" (III.ii.50). The imagery changes to darkness, disease, beasts, blood, and disrupted nature. It is chiefly through the imagery that the life-sized dramatic action becomes magnified to cosmic dimensions. Nature imagery, particularly, forms a gigantic screen of macrocosmic consequence which enlarges and intensifies Macbeth's actions and reactions. When, for example, Macbeth contemplates murder, the stars hide their fires (I.iv.50). And when Macbeth commits the murder, "the heavens, as troubled with man's act,/Threaten his bloody stage" (II.iv.5-6), creating "A great perturbation in nature" (V.i.10). Macbeth lives in an interrelated universe where nature, symbolically, participates in human suffering and punishment. Only because the nature imagery is sacramental (i.e., bearing a transcendent power) can Macbeth's bloody hands symbolically turn the green ocean red (II.ii.61-63). Enlarged to his fullest stature, Macbeth casts the cosmic shadow of a demon—"black Macbeth" (IV.iii.52), "Devilish

Macbeth" (IV.iii.117), and "hell-bound" (V.viii.3). Though the contestants are mortals, the contest is between divine and demonic powers. When we look at the imagery of the play, we see the dramatic action magnified beyond the mundane, enlarged on a cosmic screen of heaven and hell.

When Macduff discovers the murdered Duncan, he cries, "Confusion [meaning destruction] now hath made his masterpiece" (II.iii.71). A masterpiece of confusion is possible, however, only if it is placed in a frame of masterful order. With such a frame the entire play is brought into focus. The only way Macbeth can affirm himself without harming himself is by affirming the given structure of his world. This Macbeth refuses to do. A portrait of Macbeth would look like the negative of a photograph; all the whites would be blacks. His "Vaulting ambition" (I.vii.27), which should be considered a tragic flaw or weakness, becomes his strength, but a strength to be refuted by a higher strength. Indeed, as Macbeth says, "There's nothing serious in mortality" (II.iii.98) if the powers above mortality are not respected. Those who gamble that might without right endures, lose. Macbeth once was a good man. He gambled. The victory is that Macbeth lost, but the loss of a good man makes no one happy, except perhaps the witches. We would weep more easily for Macbeth than for Lady Macbeth. Macbeth was a fool, indeed a damned fool, but at least he sold his soul for golden crown to become a king and not for a gray-flannel suit to become an organization man.

Macbeth, in my opinion, is a great play, but not Shakespeare's greatest play. It is about a man and his country, not about a man and his family. Moreover, the highest power in the play is justice, not love. Nevertheless, it is a masterpiece that can best be explained, despite the masterful artistry and the creative use of language, by the mystery of pure genius, a genius familiar with the depths of evil.

Appendix

THE DOMINANT IMAGERY

The dramatic action is accompanied by poetic imagery. As the following outline reveals, the imagery functions as a symbolic shadow of the action. For example, when Macbeth is a hero fighting the enemies of Scotland, he is called an eagle and a lion. On the other hand, when he is destroying Scotland itself, he is called a hell-hound and a monster. The action is reflected and interpreted in the imagery.

Although the play contains imagery of medicine, disease, music, clothes, magic, color (all discussed throughout the play), only three major categories are summarized in this appendix, none of which is mutually exclusive: First, nature imagery, including weather, the cosmos, growth, natural and unnatural phenomena. Second, light and dark imagery, including night, day, stars, sun, candles. Third, animal imagery, including birds, beasts, reptiles, insects.

Since the central event in *Macbeth* is murder, the dominant imagery is negative, expressing destruction. The nature imagery, which shows that man's state in nature depends on more than

139

nature, reflects the violation of life. The light and dark imagery reflects the loss of the good of reason, the reason obscured by desire. And the animal imagery reflects the loss of humanity. Shakespeare places man in a cosmic setting, an interdependent world and a concerned universe where creation is sacramental (bearing the transcendent power of blessing or cursing) and where the physical world reflects the moral world. A correlation of the action and the imagery fully discloses Macbeth's moral disinheritance and disintegration.

ACT I

Scene	Action	Nature	Light-Dark	Animal
I.i	Witches meet	Storm	Fog, sunset	Cat, toad
I.ii	Macbeth defends Scotland	Storm	Sun	Eagle, lion
I.iii	Macbeth tempted	Seeds, root	Instruments of Darkness	—
I.iv	Macbeth fears Malcolm	Plant, harvest	Hidden stars	—
I.v	Lady Macbeth transforms herself	Milk, gall	Thick night, sunless morrow	Raven, serpent
I.vi	Duncan visits Macbeth	Delicate air, procreant cradle	Daylight, outdoors	Temple-haunting martlet
I.vii	Murder pact sealed	Murdered babe	—	Beast

Conclusion: Nature at its very sources is being abused. Natural light is suppressed by darkness. The subhuman (the witches) and the inhuman (Macbeth and Lady Macbeth) are forms of bestiality. The imagery reflects the central theme of fair becoming foul.

ACT II

Scene	Action	Nature	Light-Dark	Animal
II.i	Macbeth awaits zero hour	Firm-set earth	Extinguished candles (stars)	Wolf

II.ii	Macbeth murders Duncan	Murdered sleep, discolored water	—	Owl
II.iii	The murder discovered	Feverous earth	—	Obscure bird (owl)
II.iv	Night of the murder	Bloody stage (the earth), entombed earth	Strangled sun (no sunrise)	Falcon, owl, wild horses

Conclusion: Nature, symbolically murdered, suffers Macbeth's crime along with horrified humanity. The stars and the sun, symbols of guidance and knowledge, are extinguished. Evil darkens the cosmos. Man as a murderer is man as a beast. The imagery reflects murder as an unnatural crime of cosmic dimensions.

ACT III

Scene	*Action*	*Nature*	*Light-Dark*	*Animal*
III.i	Macbeth fears Banquo	Fruitless crown, barren sceptre, seed of Banquo	Dark hour	Dogs (all varieties cited)
III.ii	Macbeth's terrible dreams	Rooky wood	Seeling night, pitiful day, thickened light	Snake, scorpion beetle, crow, bat
III.iii	Banquo murdered	—	Streaks of day, cloudy evening, extinguished torch	—
III.iv	Macbeth sees Banquo's ghost	Opened graves	—	Serpent, worm, kites, bear, rhinoceros, tiger, magpies, choughs, rooks
III.v	Hecate awaits Macbeth	Storm	Foggy cloud	—
III.vi	Macduff seeks help	—	—	—

Conclusion: Nature abused becomes fruitless. More murder brings more darkness, interior as well as exterior. Animal images increase as Macbeth becomes a more ruthless beast. The imagery reflects the blind, bestial life of evil.

ACT IV

Scene	Action	Nature	Light-Dark	Animal
IV.i	Macbeth questions the witches	Nature's germens, thunder, infected air	Dark cavern, moon's eclipse, black hags	Many beasts (wolf, etc.)
IV.ii	Macduff's family murdered	Violent sea	—	Wren, owl, poor bird
IV.iii	Malcolm tests Macduff	Earth, mother, grave	Bright angels	Lamb, vulture, deer, hell-kite, chickens

Conclusion: Murder unlimited becomes geocide. Polarities of good and evil are bright angels and black hags. It is a predatory world of the vulture and his helpless prey. The imagery reflects death conquering life.

ACT V

Scene	Action	Nature	Light-Dark	Animal
V.i	Lady Macbeth sleepwalks	Sleepwalking (perturbation in nature)	Taper in the dark, murky hell	—
V.ii	Revolt against tyranny	Flower, weeds	—	—
V.iii	Macbeth heart-sick	Sear and yellow leaf, rooted sorrow	—	Geese, dogs
V.iv	Malcolm advances	Hewn boughs	—	—
V.v	Macbeth's despair and resolution	Moving grove, storm	Extinguished candle, sun	—
V.vi	Malcolm attacks	Leavy screens	—	—
V.vii	Macbeth fights	—	—	bear
V.viii	Macbeth slain by Macduff	Ripped womb, newly planted	—	hell-hound, monster

Conclusion: With supernatural power, nature (the sacred wood) becomes the Nemesis of unnatural evil; the course of nature withers tyranny and newly plants justice. When all the lights go out, including the sun, man becomes a hell-hound, a monster. The imagery reflects the death of destruction and the birth of recreation.

Glossary

Note: Some of the words listed here are also used in their modern sense. Use the modern meaning of the word if the older meaning does not make sense.

ADDITION, title
ADMIRED, amazing
AFEARD, afraid
AFFECTION, disposition
AFFEER, confirm
AN, if
ANON, immediately
AROINT, begone
ATTEND, await
CHAUDRON, entrails
CHOPPY, chapped
CLEPT, named
CLING, wither
COMPOSITION, agreement
CONCEIT, thought
CONFOUND, destroy
CONFUSION, destruction
CONVINCE, overpower
COUSIN, any relative
DEAR, dire
DOUBT, fear

FANTASTICAL, imaginary
FAVOUR, countenance
FEE-GRIEF, personal grief
FELL, cruel, scalp
GALLOWGLASS, heavily armed Irish footsoldier
GIN, snare
GOOSE, a clothes iron
GOUTS, drops
HUSBANDRY, economy
INCARNADINE, make red
KERN, light-armed Irish soldier
KIND, nature
LARGE, liberal
LIMBEC, an alembic or still
LUXURIOUS, lustful
MAGGOT-PIE, magpie
MERE, absolute
METAPHYSICAL, supernatural
MODERN, ordinary
NAPKIN, handkerchief

143

NICE, precise
NIGHTGOWN, dressing-gown
OF, by
ON, of
OWE, own
PRESENTLY, immediately
ROUND, plain
SEEL, blind
SIRRAH, term of address for inferiors
SKIRR, scour

SLEAVE, floss silk
STILL, always
THOROUGH, through
UNKIND, unnatural
VIRTUE, power
WINK AT, close eyes to
WIT, wisdom
WITH, against
WORM, snake